CHRIS HOWKINS

HEATHLAND HARVEST

THE USES OF HEATHLAND PLANTS THROUGH THE AGES

PUBLISHED BY

CHRIS HOWKINS

First published 1997

© Chris Howkins 1997

ISBN   1 901087 05 0

PUBLISHED by
Chris Howkins,
70, Grange Road,
New Haw,
Addlestone,
Surrey.
KT15 3RH

PRINTED in England by
Unwin Brthers Ltd.,
The Gresham Press,
Old Woking,
Surrey.
GU22 9LH

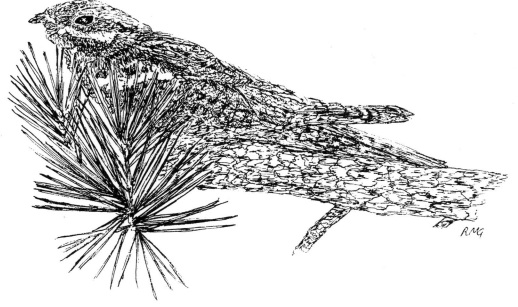

CONTENTS

Molinia
B.P.

E. pilobium

INTRODUCTION

This book highlights the uses of the special plants that create the landscapes we call heathlands. Some of these uses go back to the first peoples who came to these lands after the last Ice Age. Those were really tough hardy people and that tenacity in the people of the heaths has been recorded ever since. They've had no choice but be tough for they were considered by the rest of society to be of the lowest levels. Few writers bothered to record how they won their livings from the arid land but win one they did and by researching out the uses of the plants all manner of insights come to light as to how this was achieved. They would be fascinating themes to explore and illustrate in detail but for the moment this study concentrates upon the usefulness of the plants.

The interest and the material have been gathered over many years, having spent much of my life amid the Surrey heathlands. This became more formalised in the 1980s when the National Trust commissioned several series of promotion features, each of which included at least one with a heathland theme. Thus there are many Surrey references in this book, partly because Surrey still holds a large proportion of the country's heathland but also because there has been more chance to find and substantiate the details of usage.

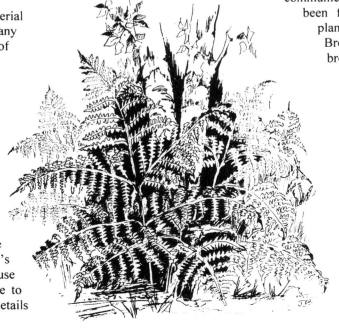

In particular the writings of two people well experienced in Surrey life have been evaluated; John Evelyn and Gertrude Jekyll. Then there is the work of numerous artists and photographers in museum collections who recorded so vividly what writers failed to mention. For the illustrating of this book three artists offered their help and their contributions are initialled, as follows: RMG for Robert McGibbon, BD for Beryl Daborn and JB for Janet Blight, to whom I am very grateful. The overall design is mine, with the informality of earlier publications which will hopefully appeal to the general reader for whom this book was made. For clarity of communication the old practice has been followed of giving English plant names a capital letter - Broom brooms is clearer than broom brooms!

WHAT ARE HEATHLANDS ?

Heathlands are divided into 'lowland' (below 300m; some authorities have 250m) and 'upland' merging often with moorland. It is with the former that this study is concerned, with those areas of acid sands and gravels and a few clays, of recent geological age, that are

deficient in nutrients and found so widely that all but a few counties have examples. The soils can be so thin that the sandstone breaks through the surface and the rain runs off rapidly, leaving them dry, just as water drains rapidly down through the gravels. These have given rise to a special covering of vegetation that can subsist on little food and water, can conserve what water it gets, and can withstand exposure to both full sun all day in the summer and icy winds all winter. In contrast there are areas where the run-off gathers into acid boggy areas and pools, some of which dry up in the summer. These require plants of a different stamina altogether.

These heathlands are an international rarity. They only occur along the north western Atlantic seaboard, stretching from the Iberian peninsula round the western European shores to Scandinavia and including the off-shore islands such as the British Isles. Thus they range through varying latitudes, with their own climatic variations, and result in each country having its own version of a heathland when all the plants and wildlife and their associations are taken into account. Those of Britain are therefore unlike those anywhere else in the world. That is why there is currently much concern for their conservation. Even in Britain there are variations from the west with its more maritime climate across to the east with its more continental climate, and from Scotland down to Cornwall. There are only about 60,000ha left, with over half in England, primarily in Cornwall, Devon, Dorset, East Anglia (Breckland), Hampshire, Staffordshire and Surrey. It is those of the southern counties that are the focus of this study but evidence has been considered, and sometimes used, from far and wide. Often it is the records of Scotland that give the details missing from the south and these have been used, with reservations of course, to explain southern uses (such as thatching with Bracken) when there seems little grounds for doubting its relevance. The northern flora is more limited than the south and so some plants were pressed into use that would have been ignored in the south where something better was available and so where there are doubts the northern material has been omitted. Even so, this study is not exhaustive and much work still needs to be done, especially in local history records where all sorts of exciting bits of information lie stored away. Extra material would be welcomed by the publisher for future use.

Illustrations: Top left and right, Marsh Gentian, for tonic medicine. Left, Bell Heather. Below, Sand Lizard

HEATHLAND OR COMMON ?

Heaths can be commons and commons can be heaths but they are not the same thing, despite popular usage of the words. *Heathland* is an ecological term to describe a particular range of habitats. *Common* is an administrative or legal term describing land over which people had (or still have) 'commoners' rights' by which they could use it. Commons can range from the seashore to mountain sides but in many southern places they are heaths, hence the confusion. The difference is only important to readers wishing to study further a particular usage and needing to know by what right, if any, the plant materials were taken.

CREATION AND CONSERVATION

The quintessential plant of the heaths is the Ling. It is a very distinctive species and the only one in its genus, so it is readily identified in the prehistoric record. Thus we are assured it has been here since Weichselian times, when the mean average temperature was just two degrees Celsius above freezing - so this plant is very tough. As the climate improved so it lost much of its terrain to invading tree cover, until the Mesolithic period when, it is now thought, man started creating clearances in the forests. These accelerated greatly in the Neolithic and Bronze Ages when the first farmers cleared much woodland to increase grazing. Without trees the soil was exposed to leaching etc. and deteriorated to the point where Ling heaths developed and extended their range into the far south. Then, in the Iron Age, the weather suddenly and dramatically turned very wet and many *Calluna* heaths became inundated with *Sphagnum* bogs. As the climate dried so the heather recolonised.

For a long time it was believed that the Ling actually made the soils more sterile by a process called 'podsolization' but Ling is currently seen as the final claimant to such soils. Once established it does not improve the soil itself and so it maintains the heathland, not only by causing chemical changes with its own litter but by its robust competition against other plants which might be soil improvers and also by facilitating

heathland fires. The early farmers soon discovered how easily such soils became exhausted and moved on, leaving the *Calluna* heaths to be their own special selves.   (see Dimbleby)

Without regular cutting or grazing (and burning in some places) the Ling ages and dies out. That is what has been happening through the twentieth century with the demise of so much of the grazing tradition, leaving the land open to invasion by Birch, Scots Pine and Oak. Restoration projects aim to increase the amount of Ling again, both for its own beauty, as it turns the landscape into rumpled blankets of purple each summer, and for the sake of the extensive range of wildlife that is dependent upon it and therefore just as threatened. The great expanses of Ling have been described as "*the last wilderness*" in the south.

Such restoration on the Continent is aided by the general public who heed polite notices asking them to keep to the paths and keep dogs under control, to save disturbing threatened wildlife and trampling the plants - and this they do with pride. In England any suggestion of self control is liable to be ignored, by those who view the heaths as 'open spaces' where their children and dogs can run wild, amid horses and mountain bikes, disturbing wildlife and causing massive erosion. There is great resistance in many places to the idea of designated routes for horse riding and cycling etc. yet these routes, which are such an attraction in some places, help save from destruction that which users find so attractive. Any sense of restriction is liable to be seen as an infringement of rights - by those who forget that the companion to rights is responsibility.

"Long live the wet and the wilderness yet!"

THE YEAR'S HARVEST

A harvest could be taken off the heathlands throughout the year, as illustrated in the table below. This table is, however, highly generalised. Not all the plants would be found on every heath. Not all the people needed all of them. Not all the people would know all the uses all the time. The timing of the seasons varies from year to year and place to place, and so forth.

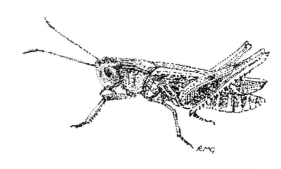

PLANT	JAN	FEB	MAR	APR	MAY	JUNE	JUL	AUG	SEPT	OCT	NOV	DEC
BIRCH Sap	X	X										
BIRCH Brooms	X	X	X	X	X	X	X	X	X	X	X	X
LING Brooms	X	X	X	X	X	X	X	X	X	X	X	X
LING Honey							X	X	X			
DODDER						X	X					
BROOM Brooms	X	X	X	X	X	X	X	X	X	X	X	X
BROOM Flowers					X	X						
BROOM Thatch					X			X	X			
SUNDEWS					X	X	X	X				
ERICA Honey					X	X	X	X				
BOG COTTON					X	X	X					
SHALLON Fruits									X	X		
BOG BEAN				X	X	X	X	X				
SWEET GALE					X	X	X	X				
BOG ASPHODEL							X	X	X			
BRACKEN				X	X	X	X	X	X			
SPHAGNUM		X	X	X	X	X	X	X	X	X	X	X
FURZE		X	X	X	X	X	X	X	X	X	X	X
WHORTLEBERRIES Fruit							X	X	X			
GRAZING		X	X	X	X	X	X	X	X	X	X	X

BIRCH

SILVER BIRCH

Betula pendula Roth

DOWNY BIRCH

Betula pubescens Ehrh

The Birch is the tree that has been in Britain longer than any other. It was here between the Ice Ages and moved back as soon as the ice melted. Then the Pine came to dominate, only to be replaced by more Birch woods. Now that the heathland Birches are no longer harvested it is highly invasive again. As far as practical uses are concerned, both past and present, the two species of Birch can be considered as one. Indeed there was a time when botanists classified them as one variable species, known as *Betula alba*.

There were times when the prehistoric landscape had a great deal of Birch, providing browsing material for the wandering herds and the accompanying hunter-gather peoples. As the latter started to settle and took to farming so the numbers of Birch must have declined due to felling and increased grazing. Consequently it is difficult to appreciate nowadays the extent to which Birch was found on the heathlands through man's history. Records imply that it was taken primarily from woodlands. Perhaps we should imagine the heaths having a few trees and isolated groves but that much of the heathland Birch was coppiced for fuel, browsing, brooms, building material etc. Obviously there would be a range of variation depending upon the size of the heathland in relation to the needs and demands of its manor.

We can be fairly certain that it would have been important to the poorer peoples as the wood has always been considered a 'cheap' timber and would have been left till last. Even then, trees infected with the Birch Bracket Fungus would have to be rejected as timber since the fungus weakens the structure of the wood. If this was caught at an early stage the tree was still desired by the charcoal-burners who could still make good 'small coals' from it, so the landowner did not lose out completely on his financial return. Nevertheless, the charcoal-burners did not pay as much for their trees as did the timber merchants.

We read that Birch was used for all manner of small domestic items which implies a wide application and large market. However, this can be misleading since early lists are an over-view and not specific to the southern heathland regions. Thus they could well have included uses from places like Scotland where there was often little else to use but Birch and Alder. What is certain is that Birch was available from earliest times and through several thousand years has been exploited and valued for a very wide range of uses, involving leaves, bark, rotten wood, sound wood, twigs, even the sap and not forgetting the bracket fungus that parasitizes the trunk.

GRAZING AND COPPICE STOOLS

Wherever there were mature Birch trees able to seed on to the heathlands there would have been a fine crop of seedlings the following spring. They certainly germinate in profusion, hence epithets like '*the Surrey weed*'. That's the tree's response to the maritime conditions in Britain, but on Continental heathlands, such as the Danish, they need a degree of nurturing.

The seedlings are palatable to herbivores, from horses down to rabbits. Current exercises at returning livestock to the heaths are revealing that the Downy Birch is grazed first, in preference to the Silver Birch, presumably because the Downy Birch protects itself from caterpillars etc. with its hairs whereas the Silver Birch has more highly developed chemical warfare, which makes it less palatable. Formerly, shepherds and village cowherds must have needed to safeguard sprouting Birch stools since they would have been very tempting to livestock - the leaves provide the richest grazing on the heaths. There's little foliage on Heather, Gorse and Broom. Perhaps grazing was permitted as growth slowed at the end of the first summer because then the saplings intended for future cropping were cut down to about 3cm from the ground. The livestock could grave it down and any stubborn stems remaining could then be billhooked off for faggots. The stumps then sprouted the following spring "*in strong and lusty tufts*" as Evelyn puts it, to grow on for besoms, kindling wood, etc. Cropping could be partial, leaving one shoot per stool to grow on for a few years until they were much desired by the wood turners for making small household items. While this was happening more shoots would spring from the stool and so regular harvesting could continue around the developing poles. If the grazier could turn his hand to making besoms and working a lathe he could make a steady living off what was otherwise described as 'barren' land. Today Birch thickets are a problem on the heaths, as they encroach upon the habitats of more desirable and threatened species.

HOUSEHOLD USES

When the cows were brought home from the heath at the end of the day so the cowherd could bring a range of raw materials from the Birch trees to satisfy everyday needs. Scrolling up a sheet of bark peeled off a tree to make a funnel is not of major economic interest, but, how invaluable it must have been when such a thing was needed. Similarly a handful of Birch spray served so well to thrash the repaired wall while the daub was still soft so that the surface was roughened to grip the final weatherproofing of lime plaster. Scrolls of the same thin young bark made useful torches if householders needed to pop outside after dark. If they were going night fishing the same came in useful and with a degree of 'country know-how' could attract the fish. Poachers found they attracted gamekeepers too! Stamp the flame out quickly and the bark blended into the natural landscape; no one had been there! Get out the tinder-box to relight it and the tinder or touchwood therein could well have been made from the Birch Bracket Fungus (*Piptoporus betulinus*). Back home strips of the fungus were nailed on to short narrow boards (pores uppermost) to serve as razor strops. In literate households flattened blocks of the fungus could be used (pores downwards) as ink blotters. When this parasite has reduced the wood to ginger coloured compost that is exactly how it was used - as seed compost:

"and of the quite consumed and rotten (such as we find reduced to a Kind of reddish Earth in superannuated hollow Trees) is gotten the best Mould for the raising of diverse Seedlings of the rarest Plants and Flowers..." (Evelyn; Silva; Ch.XVII)

Of the sound white wood was made cosmetic face powder, for 17th century men, of which Evelyn observed: *"of the whitest Part of the old Wood, found commonly in doating Birches, is made the Grounds of our effeminate farined Gallants Sweet Powder..."* The heels of their shoes were often made of Birch wood too, while it was used in the poorer homes for making the clogs; (Alder was preferred).

Weaving strips of the papery bark into punnets for fruit, such as Whortleberries, Blackberries and little wild Strawberries, could have been quite a cottage craft in early summer ready for taking the pickings to market. These devolved into our own lifetimes as the 'chip punnets' for Strawberries, Currants etc. before compressed paper took over. Parallel with this in former times were woven cones of straw, beautifully made, judging by those recorded by artists. Court records reveal some people stuffed the bottoms with Bracken to cheat customers with short measures.

Another use that has been reintroduced by Scandinavians and now being exported to Britain is the making of egg-beaters made from Birch twigs. It's a frustrating fiddly business until you've learned the knack! Take some long pliable Birch twigs, unbranched and out of leaf. Bind them round the end of a handle, projecting forwards. Bend each twig back on itself to make a loop and bind those round the handle until you have a neat ring of Birch loops, that will serve very well for beating eggs. The best handles were made of Ash twigs which are stout, smart and smooth barked.

It is the survival of knowledge of such expedients that gives such revealing insight into homes that were deemed too poor for the literate middle classes to enter and describe in words. Such uses were no doubt even more numerous and widespread in prehistoric and early historic times. Little evidence has come to light in the British Isles for Birch bark canoes, roofs, floors, shoes etc. but all are well known in other cultures, from the Scandinavians to native North Americans. It would be very odd indeed if the people of these islands were not part of that pattern, especially as Scandinavian peoples settled here. The earliest prehistoric bowls recovered by archaeologists in England were made of Birch bark. Rarely does such a perishable material survive for archaeologists to find so many questions will remain unanswered.

Birch Bracket Fungus; *Piptoporus betulinus.*

9

SELECTION OF
USES OF BIRCH TREES
PAST AND PRESENT
***
AIRCRAFT, early
BASKETS
BAVIN BANDS
BESOMS
BOATS AND CANOES
BOBBINS
BUILDING
BUS FLOORS
BOWLS and PLATES
CARS, early
CHAIRS and FURNITURE
CHARCOAL
CLOGS and SHOES
COMPOST
COOPERAGE
CORDAGE
COTTON REELS
DYE
EGG BEATERS
FAGGOTS
FIRE BEATERS
FODDER
FOOD
FUEL
GUNSTOCKS
HOOPS
HORSE JUMPS
LADLES
LIGHTING
MEDICINES
OX YOKES
PANNIERS
PITCH and TAR
PLATFORMS
PLYWOOD
RAKES
RITUALS
ROOFS
SCREWS
SHELTER BREAKS
SMOKE FOR CURING
SWALES
TANNING
TOOL HANDLES
TRACKWAYS
VINEGAR PURIFYING
WANDS
WEAPONS
WHEELS
WINE
WITHES
WOOD PULP

TAPPING FOR SAP

Few trees in the world are famous for yielding a useful sap but Birch trees can join the Rubber trees and Sugar Maples on such a list. It's the foundation of two main products: Birch Water and Birch Wine, which have been primarily of medicinal use. They have been exploited greatly in Russia, Scandinavia, and North America where the Birch is such an important tree but the British appear to have been ignorant of its virtues for many a generation and then very reluctant to adopt its usage. This has been due in part to so much of our medical knowledge being derived from ancient Greek and Roman texts, wherein the Birch does not feature greatly. Thus when William Turner produced his *New Herball* (1551) he turned to his great mentor Dioscorides (1st century AD) only to report "*I find nothing of this Byrche tree in Dioscorides*" and he found only a scant reference in Pliny (the Elder, AD 23-79). He would have done better to have turned to his contemporary, Matthiolus, (Pietro Andrea Mattioli; 1501-77) who was enthusiastic about Birch Water for breaking kidney and gall stones. Patients were laid on a bed of Birch leaves and covered over with more, with a blanket on top to trap the heat, before being dosed. Turner, however, was insultingly intolerant of Matthiolus. Apparently the Italian could be a rather difficult man in his arrogant sort of way but nevertheless he was one of the most respected physicians of his time. He did not, however, always agree with Dioscorides and that to Turner was insufferable, even though Turner himself points out errors in his mentor's writings.

Knowledge of Birch spread faster through the rest of Europe than it did in Britain so that by the time of Napoleon's campaigns his surgeon general was also enthusiastic about it, for skin, blood and urine problems including gout. Even by 1862 the English C.P.Johnson could only cite Birch Sap Wine as being good for bladder and kidney problems on the strength of reports from the Scottish Highlanders.

Two centuries before, Evelyn had delivered his *Silva* to the Royal Society and therein discussed at considerable length the tapping of Birch and other trees for sap. All practicalities were dealt with, from whether it was better to make a horizontal incision or a vertical one, whether it was better to do so near the ground or up under a bough and whether it was better on the sunny side or the shady; in reviewing the favoured dates for tapping he advised that the weather was a better guide than the calendar and offered advice he'd received on the amount it was safe to take without killing the tree. He even detailed the making a spout out of a swan or goose quill. He was in no doubt that the liquor was efficacious, (primarily for kidney and bladder stones), and then prints the recipe "*sent me by a fair Lady, and have often, and still use it:*"

"*To every Gallon of Birch-water put a Quart of Honey, well stirred together; then boil it almost an Hour with a few Cloves, and a little Lemon-peel, keeping it well scummed: When it is sufficiently boiled, and become cold, add to it three or four Spoonfuls of good Ale to make it work (which it will do like new Ale) and when the yest begins to settle, bottle it up as you do other winy Liquors.*" He offers the alternatives of sugar or raisins as sweeteners and if storing in barrels the adding of "*a small Proportion of Cinnamon and Mace bruised, about half an Ounce of both to ten Gallons, close stopped, and to be bottled a Month after.*"

Bottling required care. "*This Wine, exquisitely made, is so strong, that the common Sort of Stone-Bottles cannot preserve the Spirits, so subtile they are and volatile; and yet it is gentle, and very harmless in Operation within the Body......Care must be taken to set the Bottles in a very cool Place, to preserve them from flying; and the wine is rather for present drinking, than of long Duration, unless the Refrigeratory be extraordinarily cold.*"

Such wine is back in commercial production today, in Dorset, Inverness and Sussex. The process is still very much the same but experimentation has shown that the later dates discussed by Evelyn are too late at the Lurgashall Winery in Sussex, which produces 15,000 bottles a year. Instead of waiting till March they find they must tap as soon as the buds begin to tinge green, for once the buds have begun to unfurl it is too late. Boring must penetrate the bark and far enough into the sapwood for the spout to stay in place but not as far as the heartwood, so trunks at least nine inches in diameter are chosen. The height of the tap should be 1-2 feet above the ground after which the sap runs within ten seconds - if it doesn't, the hole is plugged and left for another day. Each tree is tapped only once every three or four years, and only a gallon of sap is taken (in about 24 hrs) as the old warnings about killing the tree have proven valid. [Johnson recalled Russian soldiers killing the trees near Hamburg in 1814 when they tapped all the trees they could find "*and intoxicated themselves with the fermented juice.*"]

According to a current recipe each gallon of sap is boiled for about 20 mins. with the peel of two lemons, one sweet orange and one Seville orange (minus all the white pith) after which it is topped up with water to return the measure to one gallon. This is then poured over three pounds of sugar and a pound of chopped raisins and stirred until all the sugar has dissolved. When it has cooled to 70°F./ 21°C. the fruit juice and yeast are added and it is left in the warm to ferment. Beer has been made from the bark, while another alcoholic drink has been distilled from the unopened leaf buds.

(Current inf. courtesy Lurgashall Winery and the Dept. of Economic Botany, Royal Botanic Gardens, Kew.)

In Eastern Europe the sap is not only a basis for beer and wine but is also a major source of sugar. Perhaps this could be introduced into Britain, especially in Scotland where attempts to recreate the ancient tree cover includes planting new Birch woods and also making them productive to increase employment opportunities.

BIRCH OIL FOR TANNING AND MEDICINE

In addition to the sap, Birch also yields a useful oil. This is found in the wood and twigs but is usually extracted from the bark. It has important medicinal uses and the tannins contained in it have been used for tanning leather. The oil was, and still is, obtained by distillation after which the liquid settles with tar at the bottom and the oil floating on top. The latter can then be taken off. It is thick brownish black with a penetrating odour that is not unpleasant - it's what gives the special smell to Russian leather. When it comes to British leather much more research is needed into exactly which trees were employed and to what extent - such a choice gets listed 'for tanning'. The fact that Russian leather was famed in part for its Birch oil smell implies that this was not available widely in Britain where the Oak became the best known source, except in Scotland where there was little Oak but plenty of Birch. The true picture may never be revealed completely in that some of our tanning was probably performed illegally and therefore secretly. This would apply to districts which, in the Middle Ages, were governed by Forest

Law as opposed to Common Law. The Forest Law was to preserve large areas of the countryside as hunting reserves, for the King's pleasure. These were not necessarily woodland and so included heathland, as in the New Forest. To this end the occupation of tanner was usually prohibited, lest anyone be tempted to convert a royal deer into a smart pair of buckskin trousers. We know from court records that such regulations were not always heeded and illegal tanning took place. To complicate matters further there is contradictory evidence as to the exact location and extent of Forest Law, not to mention its degree of enforcement, so there is plenty of work for the local historian on this topic!

Apart from leather a simpler practice was to boil up a decoction of the bark and use that as a preservative of fishing nets and ropes. This usage might have been important where heathlands come down to the sea but elsewhere tanners presumably got their Birch as a woodland rather than heathland product.

Medicinally Birch Tar Oil is still in use. It goes into creams and ointments and medicated soaps for chronic skin diseases such as eczema and psoriasis. Also, the oil from the bark has been used as a substitute for wintergreen in liniments.

An added extra comes from the Birch Bracket Fungus (*Piptoporus betulinus*) which has a cuticle over its upper surface that can be peeled off and used as a 'sticky plaster' over minor wounds.

MEDICINAL USES OF
BIRCH TREES
PAST AND PRESENT
(Not necessarily valid !)
***
Antiseptic
Baldness
Consumption
Fever
Gout
Haemorrhoids
Kidneys - Bladder - Cystitis
Muscular pain
Oedema
Rheumatism
Sedative
Skin conditions - Eczema
Sore Mouth

AMENITY VALUE

Since ancient times the beauty of these trees has been recognized and associated with appropriate spiritual forces, such as the goddess Venus and her counterparts in other cultures. Today attention turns more upon the tree's practical merits:- not too tall, not too broad, fast growing, easy to grow, wind resistant, tolerant of urban environments and so forth. In other words, ideal for planting in streets, parks, small urban gardens, suburban estates etc. except that it is not always ideal. The mass of surface roots can be a severe limitation to the successes of many an aspiring gardener and the tree's search for moisture draws it into the smallest crack of any nearby drain. Worst of all, it will never attain the stature necessary to dwarf oppressive large modern buildings and thereby return a human scale to a site. It won't reduce the impact of massed roofs in a new estate. It's a tree for screening and softening not for making an architectural statement. The dogged faith of the planners that this tree will fulfil their inappropriate expectations is quite remarkable.

With the Renaissance came interest in improving country estates, both in terms of gardens as well as parkland, and the Birch was one of the trees promoted. The Surrey Record Office holds the building accounts of Ashley House at Walton-on-Thames and we read of a payment in 1607 for *"Hawthorn, hollys, burch, Junyper, egletine and suche for settes for hedges."* They cost £5 9s 8d. What a grand hedge was made too - prickly Holly and spiny thorn to make it serviceable; evergreen Holly and Juniper for winter colour; May blossom and eglantine roses for colour and scent, plus the aroma of warm Juniper, graced throughout with standards of delicate Birch. In 1670, Meager, in his *The English Gardener* lists Birch among *"Trees fit to plant by Out-Walk sides, or otherwise."* The tree was rapidly becoming desirable in its own right, separate from the income it could earn if cropped on the estates.

An idea of how big a business this all became can be gained from the announcement made in 1781 by James Shiells, seed merchant of Parliament Street in London. He was unable to sell Birch seed that year owing to crop failure. Instead, he could offer young plants at 10/- per thousand in batches up to 200,000 or 300,000! If these were to be planted three feet apart in all directions then each acre would require 4,840 plants, he said. This means a batch of 300,000 would need about 62 acres and cost £150. It was a good deal. The same quantity as saplings two feet high from Telfords and Perfects of Yorkshire would have cost £1,125. A pricing from 1786 works out at £112 10s. Doubtless it all depended upon the size of plant just as it does today. (from Harvey; Early Gard.Cats.)

Alternatively, seed could be sown. In the 1830s that cost 4/- per bushel. Considering the tiny size of

Birch seed, that's a vast amount per bushel! How was it collected? Apart from being tiny it doesn't come in fruits that can be gathered up. Instead it is released into the wind from small cones called 'strobili'. As far as is known the method used has not changed and so today the fruiting boughs are still trimmed while the strobili are green and closed, after which they are picked off by hand and spread indoors out of draughts, to dry, upon which they release the seeds for sweeping up. As Birches fruit at an early age the strobili can be reached from the ground or from a step ladder, avoiding the hazards of climbing in such a lissome tree.

(Inf: Tony Waddell, Forestry Research Station; Alice Holt.)

Whereas once the noble landowners of the realm could show off their square miles of countryside for being just that, it gradually became necessary to view land in more economic terms. With these changes came the notion and fashion for 'Improvement' of the land, leading to the pioneering works of the 'Agricultural Revolution'. Although both terms are being reassessed critically at present there was undoubted change. In due course the landowning class came to include new wealthy industrialists who had an eye to making money. Some heathlands went under the plough to feed the new industrial towns while others became plantations for raw materials. Sweet Chestnut and Birch were popular on poor soils and served the needs of the industrialists themselves - the use of Birch in steelworks has been noted and to this can be added the copper refineries of South Wales where molten copper was stirred with fresh Birch poles, which prevented the formation of oxides and thereby led to a purer product. Up in Lancashire the famous cotton mills required thousands of bobbins, spools and reels, which were made of Birch wood. Today's Birches are valued more for amenity and conservation work, even if they do have to be kept in check. Some will always be needed as part of the desired habitat of threatened wildlife; the Tree Pipit, for example, is a very desirable little bird, that needs Birches as song perches. (illustrated previous page)

In addition to amenity values the trees are of considerable value to wildlife conservation. Although, not a topic for this book, many a reader will need reassurance that clearing Birch off the heathlands in the effort to save this precious habitat, does not aim to exterminate the tree from such sites. It wouldn't be possible anyway, as those tiny seeds would come blowing back in. A mature fruiting Birch will yield over a million such seeds in one season. The Birches have been on the heathlands for so many thousands of years that hundreds of species of wildlife have adapted to them being part of the habitat and for this reason Birches are among the more important of British trees to the wildlife. The aim of the conservationists is to bring them back under control to create a more balanced habitat and to do so in aesthetically pleasing ways. Surely there is little to rival winter sunshine breaking through thin mist to light up a mature Silver Birch glazed with hoar frost; the sharp green of the unfurling leaves in dense thickets below the blueness of a spring sky; the silver trunks taking golden hues of a sunset reflected in the black peaty waters of a heathland pool; the vibrant gold of a Birch laden autumn. All these pleasures can be kept and still suit the wildlife. The Woodlark (illustrated) is another bird that uses mature Birches as song perches. Any reader who has paused on a crisp spring morning to listen to a nearby Woodlark in full song has had a rich experience indeed.

MINOR USES

Finally, just one more example from the southern heathland country of a minor practical use - the footscrapers used at all classes of domestic doorway and churches. It was rather like an upturned besom with the handle driven into the ground. That handle had to be far longer, so that it projected high enough to support the hands while the mud was being wiped off the feet on the besom part down at ground level. Worn-out besoms were often put to this final use having been provided with a new longer handle - and very good they were too.

"The Highlanders of Scotland make everything of it; they build their houses, make their beds and chairs, tables, dishes and spoons; construct their mills; make their carts, ploughs, harrows, gates and fences, and even manufacture rope of it. The branches are employed as fuel in the distillation of whisky, the spray is used for smoking hams and herrings, for which last purpose it is preferred to every other kind of wood. The bark is used for tanning leather, and sometimes, when dried and twisted into a rope, instead of candles. The spray is used for thatching houses; and, dried in summer, with the leaves on, makes a good bed when heath is scarce."

(J.C.Loudon; *An Encyclopaedia of Trees and Shrubs*; 1842)

LING
or
HEATHER

Calluna vulgaris (L.) Hull

What could be more grand than a breezy walk along the sandy paths through purple acres of flowering Heather, dotted with golden Birches below a blue sky? It's a popular pleasure, judging by the numbers of people and their dogs doing just that. Some of us even love it wild and wintery with the westerlies hounding over. Our ancestors knew it well whatever the weather, particularly the broom-maker, the turf cutter, the beekeeper and the grazier, for they all used the Ling directly, as did less frequent visitors looking for medicines, dyes, cut flowers and gruets for brewing. There was not a month of the year when the Ling couldn't provide a harvest for someone. The more significant of these, in terms of economic importance, are introduced below, except for the making of besom brooms which is in a separate chapter.

Heathers are sometimes called heaths, as per their habitat and this duality has existed since the times of the Saxons who had just the word *haeth* to name both. In Saxon place names *haeddre* is believed to mean heather. Through the Middle Ages this became *hadder, hather, or hathir* and then *hedder* (the dd pronounced th) until the 18th century gave us the present spelling. As for Ling - that came with the Danes and Vikings for it is Scandinavian; *lyng* in Norse; by the 13th century it is being written *link*. Some authorities will not commit themselves to its meaning while others connect it with *lig*, the Saxon word for fire because the turf was used for fuel. Its use for besom brooms gave rise to other Saxon names such as Bazzom and Bissom (and even Broom to confuse us today with *Cytisus scoparius*). Whatever it was called by the Celts seems to have given rise to such names as *Grig, Griglans* and *Griglum* and in the Celtic Cornish language it is *Gruglon.*

HEATHER AND BEES

Honey from heather is one of those products that is still well known today - thick and flavoursome with little air bubbles in it. There is another product though, that was once valued even more highly, and that was beeswax. *Calluna* in bloom provides a rich source of nectar and is attractive to bees for making honey and with that come the vast supplies of wax that were needed, so beekeepers have valued the heathlands for thousands of years.

"This little poore creature the Bee, doth not onely with her laboure yeeld unto us her delicate and most healthy Hony, but also with the good example of her painefull diligence and travaile, encourageth man to labour and take paines according to his calling." (Barnaby Goodge; 1577)

Bees would not have been commonplace on the earliest heathlands because there was neither food nor shelter. It wasn't until the climate after the last Ice Age had warmed sufficiently to support a range of nectar bearing flowers throughout the summer months that bees would have been able to expand their range into this corner of Europe - there was still no English Channel to make Britain an island. Even then, where heather was the dominant plant for many square miles there would only have been food for the bees for a few weeks each year. Therefore they would have been found round the fringes where better soils supported a wider range of plants. Similarly, it was here that shelter could be found - bees make their nests in holes. Opportunities to utilise natural or animal holes in the ground would have been very limited (there were no rabbits for example) and so bees would have been found where there were large old trees complete with hollows. Prehistoric man learnt to seek out and raid these nests, not just for the honey but also the wax which was used in bronze casting for his axe-heads etc. Then he learnt to imitate natural nest sites so that he could have better control over the bees and so, over 4,000 years ago, man started beekeeping.

As a beekeeper, man started providing natural nest sites with his own hollow logs and then by weaving Willow into a basin or 'skep' which could be plastered over with clay or dung to prevent draughts and rain entering through the little chinks in the weaving. Pieces of stick were wedged across the interior from which the bees could hang their combs. In due course weaving was replaced by coiling. Straw or grass was twisted into ropes and bound with the bark of Honeysuckle, Bramble or Willow, and coiled round to make the dome. This avoided all those draughty little chinks but some were still plastered to keep out the rain or else they were given

a sheltering roof. By the 15th century special alcoves or 'boles' were built into house and garden walls in which to stand the skeps for protection while cottagers who had to keep their skeps out in the open provided them with thatched shelters, ideally made from Rye straw (as it was so long, and cheap). By the 19th century William Cobbett instructed that these should be replaced every three or four months but this was obviously an ideal rather than a necessity for those in some old paintings look decidedly decrepit!

Such skeps were so effective that the design persisted for thousands of years and so they are immediately recognisable in even the earliest of illustrations. It did not, however, utilise the available space efficiently and it precluded access for management purposes by the beekeeper. It would be better if made rectangular with moveable sections but the bees defeated early versions of this by cementing it all together. Part of their natural behaviour is to collect resinous substances from plant buds and use it as a cement (called propolis or 'bee glue') to make their nest hole secure and free from draughts. Thus they sabotaged moveable parts in the same way. It wasn't until 1851 that this problem was overcome, by Revd. Lorenzo Lorraine Langstroth, an amateur beekeeper in Pennsylvania. He invented the 'bee space' which was a quarter inch gap between the combs that was found to be wide enough to allow bees through but too wide for them to cement with propolis or in which to build comb. Other apiarists developed the idea further into the modern hives of today. These designs meant bees no longer had to be killed at harvest time as had previously been the case.

Killing was necessary to get at the contents of the skep and became a matter of standing the skep over a shallow pit in which sulphur was added to burning material. The fumes choked the skep and the bees fell out. Harvesting began at Michaelmas (29th September) when the heaviest skeps were destroyed for their load of honey and wax. The middle weight skeps were kept, in which their bees overwintered. The lightest skeps were also destroyed because they did not contain enough food reserves to feed the bees through the winter. The contents of comb, wax and honey were ripped out and crushed all together in a long linen 'poke' through which the honey could be strained.

By the 17th century public opinion was turning against killing the bees. They were considered one of God's very special creations and were practically sacred. The alternative was to invert the full skep and place an empty one over it to make a sphere and then to rattle the bottom skep until the bees had fled into the upper one. This was not always successful! The new Langstroth hive was built in storeys which meant extra levels or 'supers' could be built above the

*f bees stay at home
Rain will soon come;
f they fly away,
Fine will be the day.*
   (Traditional lore)

*"Of all the creatures which are
behovefull for the use of man,
there is none more necessarie,
wholesome, or more profitable
than the Bee, nor any lesse
troublesome, or less chargeable.
To speak then first of the nature
of Bees; it is a creature gentle,
loving, and familiar about the
man which hath the ordering of
them, so he come neate, sweet,
and cleanely amongst them;
otherwise, if hee hath strong,
and ill smelling savours about
him, they are curst and
malicious, and will sting spitefully."*
   (Gervase Markham)

**Illustration - Skeps on their stools
under their Rye straw roofs.**

summer hive for the bees to move into and be separated off from their earlier combs below. This increase in space had the added advantage of deterring the bees from swarming. Under improved management harvesting was started at the end of July and lasted until the middle of September. The bees were left alone from 1st November until 1st April.

BEESWAX

It is very difficult today to appreciate how important bees have been in the past just from the point of view of providing man with wax. Today's wax comes from a variety of sources but for thousands of years honeybees were the prime or only source. It had a wide range of uses from candles to polish, from the basis of ointments to being a lubricant and waterproofer. It is secreted between scale-like plates on the underside of the abdomen of the worker bee and is used to build and repair the honeycomb and to cap the cells once they are full of honey. Worker bees are responsible for these tasks through a particular stage in their life cycles, starting when they are 10-16 days old, until superseded by the duty of receiving the nectar and pollen being brought back by the foraging workers. In due course they will become foragers themselves.

Although many cultures, such as the Greek and Roman, held bees sacred, it was the coming of Christianity to Britain that created an immense demand for beeswax, for making the church candles. The pre-Reformation Church in England used more lights than did any other region of Christendom, "owing probably to the greater gloom of our climate." The Church viewed bees as a model of chastity and so candles came to symbolise Christ born of the Virgin. A medieval Welsh document stated boldly that *"the origin of bees is from Paradise....therefore the Mass cannot be said without the wax,"* and for mass in the great churches there could be fifty or more candles at the High Altar. There were more at the side altars, at the altar of the Lady Chapel, at the altars in the chantry chapels, and more candles lighting up the painted and carved images of which the most important focused attention upon the great rood or crucifix which was the focal point of the church.

Medieval churches on great feast days were glorious with light. It must have been stunning to those who came from dark hovels where even a humble rush light was a luxury. It must have been horrific to little children looking up at a dead man nailed on a cross with the glass inlays in his eyes glittering in the candlelight. Even little country churches like Spelsbury in Oxfordshire had many altars and lights which are recorded in the churchwardens' accounts, surviving from 1525-39. The fullest list, of 1531, gives the light, its cost and the day that cost was to be met. The list, which may not be complete, impresses upon us the extent of the demand and its importance in the parishioners' year:-

Trinity light - Candlemas Day - 22s 8d
Our Lady's light - Annunciation - 4s
Hersse light - any date before Allhallowtide - 16s 10d
St. Nicholas's light - 16s 2d
St.George's light - St.Matthias Day - 22s 10d
St.Clement's light - St.Clement's Eve - 5s 7d
St.Katherine's light - St.Thomas of Canterbury -
8s 4d plus three and a half strikes of barley.
[Strike - usually 1 bushel but could be half]
St.Erasmus's light - St.Stephen's Day - 4s 8d plus a
sheep worth 20d and 2 bushels of barley
St.Christopher's light - New Year's Eve - 4s 4d and
2 bushels barley.
St.Anthony's light - Shrove Monday - 14s
St.Michael's light - St.Michael's Day - 2s and
4 bushels barley.
St.Andrew's light.

The administration of the above required two wardens, who submitted annual accounts. (Cox; 164-5) At least the burden of the costs was spread throughout the year. Multiply this impression through the thousands of medieval parish churches and we begin to glimpse aspects of medieval life which are otherwise rarely noted.

The cost of wax was the greatest of all charges met by the English medieval church. To get so much the parishioners were taxed in wax (or honey) as part of their tithes or they paid rents in wax. It was only the combined effort of all the parishioners' small hives that kept the churches lighted. People bequeathed money to their church specifically for lights, often specifying the weight of the candle they had in mind, or else they bequeathed a field from which the sale of the crops was intended to fund lights. The church at Cowfold, Sussex, owned nine oxen and four cows which they farmed out to raise funds for church lighting - two of the cows sustained four tapers in honour of

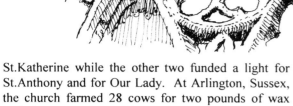

St.Katherine while the other two funded a light for St.Anthony and for Our Lady. At Arlington, Sussex, the church farmed 28 cows for two pounds of wax each but even those fifty six pounds of wax a year wouldn't have gone very far. (See Cox)

The great size of some of the candles is quite overwhelming today. The Paschal candle, lit during a special ceremony from the newly blessed fire on Easter morning and remaining in the sanctuary until Ascension Day, weighed 200 pounds or more, which has been calculated to be a year's work for 20,000 bees. The great font candle was lit during another solemn ceremony at the blessing of the font on the eve of Easter and Whitsun and was lit at all subsequent baptisms, so that must have been quite a size.

For all the major ceremonies the candles had to be of wax. For general lighting and lesser services such as mattins it was permissible to use tallow (animal fat), resin mixtures and yellow or re-used wax. It was the same in monastic houses where many lights were needed because activities persisted at intervals throughout the night. Tallow was permitted for this use except in their churches where again candles had to be of beeswax, though there might be only one candle at the High Altar. It was a different matter if the monastery housed the tombs of important nobles or royalty requiring votive lights at all times. Westminster Abbey, for example, had to find 1,434 pounds of beeswax per year once it had to provide votive lights at the tombs of Richard II, Henry III, V and VI and Queen Eleanor. Special processions must have caused quite a problem - the funeral of Henry V, for example, had sixty bearers of beeswax torches and that lot weighed a total 870 pounds - or about the weight of five men!

The lights were made by monks, other monastery workers and the servants of the great houses (which used candles as clocks - six per day marked off in twenty minute intervals). They couldn't meet demand and so chandlery became a specialised occupation by the 13th century. At that time they had become so well established as to be one of London's great trade Guilds. There is mention then of their Hall which was in Gresham Street. It fell to the great fire of 1666 but has been rebuilt, several times. Today the Worshipful Company of Wax Chandlers ranks number twenty in the City's order of precedence. They have as their grace:-

> For thy creature the bee,
> The wax and the honey,
> We thank thee, O Lord.

The late flowering of the heather must have been a wonderful bonus in many areas as it extended the working season of the bees. There was little else for the bees to work since many of the early autumn bee plants we might think of today, such as the Michaelmas Daisies, were not introduced into this country until after the Reformation. By then the high demand for beeswax had fallen. The Reformation banned altar candles, banned chantry lights, banned wax effigies, and the monasteries were closed. It was the monasteries that had developed beekeeping. The responsibility fell ultimately to the cellarer who usually kept his skeps in the curia or outer court. It was he who would have initiated the procession bearing the skeps on planks out towards the heathlands for an end of season bonus to a vital harvest.

HEATHER HONEY

Honey was the nectar of the gods - sweeter than anything else in Britain for thousands of years; nutritious, healing, and one luxury that the Church didn't frown upon - unless you got drunk on the mead made from it.

The simplest skeps stood on stools with holes through their seats to allow the bees access.

By the 16th century entrances were being contrived in the base of the skeps, enabling them to be stood on solid surfaces.

Honey is largely made up of sugars (c.70-80%) plus minerals, amino acids and vitamins of the B-complex. Worker bees suck out the nectar from eight little swellings below the stamens in the base of the Ling flower and then in special parts of their stomachs they mix it with enzymes to form honey. This is regurgitated by the worker bees when they return to the hive and pass it over to a different grade of worker who packs it into the comb cells. A worker will visit some two million flowers to make a pound of honey and that requires some 25,000 trips back to the hive, at a speed of about 20 kph. At least *Calluna* produces masses of flowers very close together and it has got to be *Calluna* if the honey is to be called 'heather' honey; *Erica* and *Daboecia* don't count, although the bees may well have collected from them at the same time. Honey is invariably made from a mixture of nectars from different flowers and that would certainly be true around the southern heathlands. In upland regions apiarists can take their hives to such a high altitude that there is only *Calluna* flowering and then a very pure honey can be obtained. This is probably the origin of the false notion that heather only produces nectar if it is growing at altitudes in excess of 300m. What is true is that *Calluna* is very variable in nectar production. The flowering period is from July to September but nectar is released for only part of that time and even that is not predictable. Every three to five years it goes to the extreme and produces a glut of the stuff, rather like Oak and Beech trees having a 'mast year' every three or four. The trees probably fruited more regularly in the early Middle Ages or else it wouldn't have been possible to work the manorial system of pannage. Perhaps the heather was more consistent then too. Despite this variability there is normally a reasonable flow most years and so people in places like the New Forest are still able to market their famous honey.

One of the problems of trying to work heather is that it flowers late and thereby fails to synchronise well with the life cycles of the hive. Encouraging them to carry on working it can leave the bees in a poor state to try and survive the winter but this was probably of little concern in the days when so many skeps were destroyed at the end of the season anyway. Today's apiarists show far greater concern over the well being of their bees. They are, after all, very valuable in so many ways, including the accidental service of pollination. Now we have learned how to manage life in the hives to extend the forage season without causing harm.

Another problem with heather honey is that it is thixotropic, which means it is a jelly rather than a liquid. This makes it difficult to extract from the comb cells, unless it is first agitated. Modern technology has overcome that problem. Formerly the combs were removed and crushed inside straining cloths, under special presses. Nowadays it is not essential to follow either practice as there is once again demand for honey still in the comb, known as 'cut-comb honey', and for this heather is ideal simply because the jelly does not run out.

The insatiable demand for beeswax from the Roman Catholic Church through the Middle Ages ensured there was always copious supplies of honey. Sometimes the Church wanted both, as in this Surrey record of lands that included heaths:-

Fortunately honey had no rivals at that time as a sweetener for although cane sugar was available from Norman times it was twenty times more expensive. Herbal sweeteners were known and used, such as Angelica, *Angelica archangelica*, Sweet Ciceley, *Myrrhis odorata* and Liquorice, *Glycyrrhiza glabra*.

Meadow Pipit habitat

Some of the honey was used up as medicine, the value of which had been known since ancient times. The Roman soldiers had carried honey with them to use as a vulnerary (wound dressing). This practice was valid. The bees put an enzyme into the honey which has an antibacterial action which does not have adverse side effects upon the healthy tissue surrounding the wound, and a honey dressing doesn't dry up. Honey was exploited too for coughs, sore throats, and other respiratory problems and it is still an important demulcent and sweetener in British medicine, mostly in linctuses and cough mixtures. However, the British Pharmacopoeia warns, *"honey should not be given to infants because of the risk of causing infant botulism."* This is due to honey having been identified as a carrier of the spores of the offending *Clostridium botulinum*.

(see S.S.Arnon et al; Honey and other environmental risk factors for infant botulism; *J. Pediatr*; 1979; 94: 331-6)

As with other medicines (see Sundew) early preparations were developed by fermentation into alcoholic drinks in their own right. In this case it was *mead*, which is the world's oldest alcoholic drink. It came to be flavoured with herbs and spices which was a speciality of the Welsh physicians in the early Middle Ages. They called it *meddyglyn* (by combining *meddyg* meaning medicinal, with *llyn* for liquor). Eventually the Welsh yielded this to the English as *metheglin* (earliest ref. 1533) and it became very popular, especially when spiced. That's how Elizabeth I liked it - with herbs and spices. A version using apples became known as *cyser* and a recipe with mulberries made *morat*. Alternatively, spices and unfermented honey could be added to wine for *clare*, *clary* and *claret* which were orginally (before c.1600) yellowish or light red wines, as opposed to the true red and white wines. Otherwise the surplus was fermented into mead.

HEATHER IN MEDICINES

When it came to healing the bodily ills of the heathland folk Ling was rather limited but had the one great virtue of providing an antiseptic, both for external and internal use. The best part to use was the fresh flowering shoots so availability was limited. Externally, a decoction was used as a facial wash and cleanser for skin conditions including acne while the leaf juice has been used as eye drops. Internally, its prime antiseptic use was, and still is, for the kidneys and urinary system, for cystitis, urethritis, etc. Knowledge of this seems to have been widespread, wherever Ling grows (despite not being well documented in the early classical writings for not being an abundant plant in those regions). Thus it has an entry in K'Eogh's Irish herbal of 1735 but did anyone follow this through? -

"About a half pint of decoction in spring water drunk warm, is very good against stone in the bladder if taken for thirty days. After which, the patient must take a bath made of a decoction of it, and this process must be often repeated."

As with all old herbal remedies, Ling should not be tried without seeking professional advice first. Drinking the decoction affects the circulatory system as it contains compounds that constrict the blood vessels and thereby cause a rise in blood pressure and affects the heart. While it's in the blood it cleanses and so has been popular for gout, often as 'heather flower tea', and for some other rheumatic and arthritic conditions. The tea is weakly sedative so use appropriately, such as bed time when some people find it helps insomnia and for which it is still listed in the British Pharmacopoeia. That also lists a preparation for reducing appetite but in the past the heathland folk had little concern for slimming. They were more likely to use Ling for stomach ache as it stimulates the production of bile, for which it still has official listing today.

(The section on honey includes medicinal matters too.)

HEATHER IN DRINK

They could certainly have a good drink out on the heathlands since heather makes fine ale. Instead of the basic recipes of today those for medieval ale varied from district to district depending upon which other brewing herbs (known as gruets) were available because quite a number went into the brew. The basics were malt, fresh water, yeast and sweetener to which the gruets were added. For sweetener there was usually lots of Angelica, *Angelica archangelica*. This was countered with bitter herbs, (instead of the later Hops) such as Alecost, *Tanacetum balsamita*, Mugwort, *Artemisia vulgaris*, Alehoof, *Glechoma hederacea* and Yarrow, *Achillea millefolium*. Other herbs could include Nettles, *Urtica dioica*, Agrimony, *Agrimonia eupatoria*, Dandelion flowers, *Taraxacum officinale*, Meadowsweet (originally Meadsweet from its use in mead), *Filipendula ulmaria*, Betony, *Stachys officinalis*, Elder berries, *Sambucus nigra*, and Bog Myrtle, *Myrica gale* (see separate section). The purpose of some bitter herbs was to help preserve the brew (replaced by Hops). Heather did just that:-

"*About Shenston, as I was inform'd by the worthy Mr Frith of Thorns, they frequently used the Erica vulgaris, heath or ling, instead of hopps to preserve their beer, which, as he also told me, gave it no ill tast.*"

(Robert Plot; Natural History of Staffordshire; 1686)

Once Hops, *Humulus lupulus*, came into use Heather ale was made more simply, as per today, by boiling the flowering tops in a little water for an hour, straining it and adding Hops, Ginger and golden syrup. Yeast is added after the mixture has been boiled and strained and cooled. After a few days' fermentation the ale is taken off, leaving the yeast deposit behind.

A quotation in the Oxford English Dictionary under 'heather' informs us from 1633 that in the north, "*They dry their malt with ling, or heath....*" No doubt that gave it a distinctive flavour too. A similar usage from the south was not found for this study.

HEATHER FOR FUEL

Turf nowadays suggests grass, whether for lawns or in a sporting context, but in the days before railways brought cheap coal into rural areas, turf meant sods of heather roots cut from the heath. This is one case where heath and common could in effect be the same, for cutting turf was one of the ancient commoners rights - the right of *turbary*, from the Latin 'tourbe' for turf. It was being documented in this name by the 13th century, although the use of such fuel must surely be prehistoric. The right was formalised in the Law of Turbary in 1567. There is an unexpected connection with paving because flagstones or flags derive from the Norse *flaga* meaning cut turves.

Ultimately turf became the fuel of the very poor but with little else to burn it was highly valued. It became of great social consequence during the period of the Enclosure Acts of the 18th and early 19th centuries when many traditional cutting grounds suddenly went into private ownership.

Many parishes, already straining to maintain the poor, made new fuel arrangements, as in Middlesex at Charlton and Sunbury-on-Thames where a new Charity was created. It set aside 46 acres of heathland to continue fuelling the poor after the Enclosure Award of 1800.

The turves themselves were the matted roots and ground litter of the heather. Today stands of heather are often dotted with tussocks of grasses etc. which would have been grazed out in former times. Ideally the plants needed to be young with short growth as these had the best root systems for binding the turves together. This sort of growth, on a large scale, is rarely seen on the heathlands of today because of the decline in two other practices that kept the heather short, namely, grazing it and cutting it for brooms.

It was in May, June and July that the turves were cut and turned over to dry. As the best turves came from the wettest parts of the heath the drying process was important. The acid water delayed the processes of decay, allowing thicker layers of 'peat' to build up to make the better turves. After drying they were carted home and stacked for winter use, providing somebody had not stolen them in the meantime. They were vital to the local economy and therefore very desirable, so theft must have been a real threat. An example may be read in the *Deposition Book* of Richard Wyatt, Justice of the Peace at Kingston-upon-Thames, who in August 1722 found John Portsmouth before him. He had gone out onto the common at Egham and carted off a load of turves cut by John Watts, a local labourer. News of this got to Watts who reached the site in time to accost Portsmouth coming back for a second load. Portsmouth announced that he'd take what he liked off the common. Watts knew his rights and turned to the law.

were sufficiently affluent to be able to afford coal and could therefore sell off their quota of turf. Some of the new private landowners who had enclosed the commons could also have been selling off turves to the poor who formerly had them by right. They cost, in the first couple of decades of the 19th century, seven shillings per thousand, when a labourer's wage might be eleven shillings.

Cutting was performed with a spade designed specifically for the job but that design varied from district to district. A common version had a stout cross bar to the handle upon which the worker could throw his weight in order to cut through the roots. The blade was somewhat heart-shaped and fixed to the handle at an angle appropriate for a good stomach thrust! The whole tool is unusually heavy, to help do the job, but lighter versions have been seen in museum collections, some without the cross-bar top, some with a cutting flange. To use any other tool could be an offence; there was a penalty of ten shillings per offender levied in Dorset.
(Court Books of Moreton Manor; 1810).

There must have been a considerable risk of such incidents since in many places limits were imposed upon the number of turves a commoner could cut. In the New Forest totals ranged between 2,000 and 6,000 annually. The ideal was 4,000-5,000 to fuel one home for a winter but many were restricted to just 2,000, so don't imagine the family sitting cosily round a fragrant peaty fire all winter. It was used sparingly to give a steady but rather gentle heat, so it had to be boosted for bringing pots and kettles to the boil, by adding a 'hurrier' such as a handful of Furze or Bracken.

Turves could be bought so obviously some people cut them to earn part of their living. In later times this could imply that people with rights of turbary

Just as Furze was taken to fuel the whole district so turf was used as fuel by communities beyond the heath. The townsfolk of Poole had rights to cut turf on Canford Common. Wareham, also in Dorset, obviously had similar rights as it was hot turf ashes thrown on a dung heap that caused the famous and highly destructive fire in the town in 1762. From the nearby Stoborough School comes the unusual record that the headmaster was allowed to take 10,000 turves a year off Stowborough Common. (Hutchins, J; *The History and Antiquities of the County of Dorset*; 3rd ed.; 1861. Other Dorset inf. supplied by Tom Goss, BTCV, Dorset.)

Each turf measured about nine inches wide and twice as long. As for the thickness, it has been recorded at three quarters of an inch but this proved difficult to achieve when tested. It was so thin the turf fell apart, yet on many heathlands that is about all there is to slice off the underlying sand. As with so many seemingly simply country tasks there is a considerable input of experience and practised dexterity. No wonder greater value was put on turves from wet areas - where the vegetation would have built up to a greater thickness.

Stripping the turves off the sand by the thousand would soon have created a useless desert but long ago our ancestors learned how to maintain the resource. They took out every third turf in a row and staggered the rows to create a chequer board effect. Thus each of the thousands of turves was cut separately rather than cutting a long strip and chopping it into sections. This left sandy patches surrounded by turf and therefore less exposed to erosion and the heather soon grew back and was ready for cutting again in six or seven years. That meant that a household taking 5,000 turves on a seven year rotation would need nearly an acre of heathland but when losses due to rock, trees, bushes etc. are taken into account then the estimate becomes even closer to an acre, except of course that by taking every third turf a total of three acres was needed. This must have been an important limiting factor in the development of heathland communities but one that is rarely commented upon. By the time Jekyll wrote her *Old West Surrey* in 1904 turf cutting was being described as a 'privilege'.

UP ON THE ROOF

There are plenty of references to heather being used for thatching but how exactly was it done? There were, apparently, two options - either to use it like the straw or reed thatch familiar today, or, to slab over the roof with turves. In either case, finding an old description of methods employed has proved difficult.

Photographs of turf roofs all seem to be associated with the Arts and Crafts Movement, leaving a question mark over the

degree to which the old ways were followed. None of the photographs revealed how the turves were laid. It would seem reasonable that they should overlap, like tiles or Horsham slabs yet in some cases it looked as though they were butted side by side. Surely this would not have been water proof as the peaty content would shrink in dry weather leaving gaps. In some cases the pitch of the roof does not look adequate for shedding the rain fast enough to prevent absorption and a considerable increase in weight; poorer homes in the past would not have had a very strong roof timbers below. Further, the turves were used as cut, with longish heather stems protruding all over - just right for catching snow and increasing weight again. Where is there a good description of roofing with turves in the southern counties?

A detailed description of thatching with heather in the south also proved elusive. The most detailed description came in fact from Scotland (1831) but as thatching has been practised since prehistoric times there are numerous regional variations anyway yet at the same time the basic principles had become established. At least this Scots writer was himself a thatcher and should have known what he was talking about, although his account raises as many questions as it answers!

Firstly, Mr Collier records an *increase* in its use at that time in Aberdeenshire as a result of improved thatching techniques. It was the technique together with the quality of the heather and the pitch of the roof that would determine ultimate lasting quality. The best was expected to last 20-30 years (comparable to straw thatch). The pitch for a building twelve feet across inside, needed to be six inches above the square. This increased by two inches for every extra foot of internal dimension. The best material was from dry sites where the Ling had been pulled (to leave a tuft of root) rather than cut. This could be done throughout the year but was avoided if possible between June and August when it was more sappy. Stems needed to be 18-20 inches long and unbranched - which is fine in the cooler wetter north but he wouldn't have liked the southern stuff so much as it tends to branch earlier. It was then bound in sheaves and laid flat to compress it straight as it dried out for three or four days. Once on the roof the heather was sometimes held down against gales with 'rope-yarn' but was liable to be eaten through by rodents; in the south there are references to making rope out of the twisted stems of both Birch and Ling and maybe this was their purpose.

Thatch was applied sometimes directly on to the roof timbers but more often there was a basic covering of tiles or turf. He anticipates queries about using both tiles and thatch by explaining that the porous tiles absorbed one seventh of their dry weight in water which then shattered during hard frosts. That would have applied to parts of the southern counties in those past decades when winters were so much colder that oxen could be roasted on the frozen Thames.

Thatching began at the eaves and worked sideways in horizontal layers instead of the vertical strips he says he would have created for straw thatching. The first layer overhung the wall by a hand's breadth and the second layer overhung that, to create the eaves, which were trimmed off horizontally with a large knife to conclude the task. From the eaves thatching progressed up the roof at the same pitch as the roof, working in blocks four feet wide, starting with the ladder two feet from the right end, and working from left to right. Then the ladder was moved to the left and another block was worked up to abut that already positioned on the right. The two had to be carefully bonded. Once five layers had been added the ladder was repositioned over the eaves to allow for reaching further up the roof. The first, second, third and fifth layers were bedded in clay of *"a sufficient quantity to make them adhere to each other"* since the eaves suffered most from exposure and so thereafter clay was used more sparingly, for every third layer. The turf or tiles beneath stopped the clay dropping through into the room while references from elsewhere, including the south, are to Furze, Bracken, rushes, straw and hay being so used. It sounds as though using the clay effectively and efficiently was where skill and experience came to the fore. An experienced eye and well-practised skill also sound crucial when we read that, *"In order to carry off the rain more readily, it is necessary to give the roof, or rather the rib, a little swell towards the middle,"* by using longer lengths of heather. It must have been easy to get a messy hump!

Once all the heather stems had been laid, with their cut ends tilted 25°-30° upwards to accelerate run-off, then the ridge was sealed. For this a mixture of clay and chopped straw was packed into place. Finally *"The whole surface of the work ought then to be gone over with a pair of scissors, cutting off only, however, the loose detached fibres."* [Scissors also meant shears in those days!]

(From Collier, John; *On Thatching with Heath*; Prize Essays and Transactions of the Highland Society of Scotland; 1831)

HORTICULTURAL USAGE

Heathers, heather gardens, and companion planting with dwarf conifers are all very much part of the garden scene today. Indeed, it is very big business to the horticulture trades and those dependent upon them; it is estimated that fifteen million *Callunas* are grown each year. This is a relatively new fashion for It was only in the early 19th century that garden writers began to record the introduction of heathers into garden schemes. Earlier than that they had been appreciated as part of the natural landscape and although 'landscape gardens' became fashionable they were not necessarily on suitably acid sandy soils. Gradually through the 19th century species from several genera were introduced on to the commercial market. Thus by 1900 when Gertrude Jekyll's influential *Home and Garden* was published she was able to note that *"There are so many beautiful kinds that it is hard to resist getting a larger number of varieties that look well together."* Nevertheless she urges restraint and preferred *"the wild Calluna to be in chief abundance,"* / *"for the sake of its quiet leaf colouring."* (pp.94/99)

If she had known what an array of different *Calluna* cultivars would be available a hundred years later she would have been quite astonished. Today there are 1713 different *Callunas* listed on the International Register. However, of these only 735 have been validly published and described; the others are either early names, or synonyms, or have not yet been fully accepted. Even so, 735 is quite remarkable when it is remembered that the genus *Calluna* has only one species in it and therefore it is not possible to breed new cultivars by hybridizing one closely related species with another, as is the normal practice with so many thousands of our garden plants. Instead today's great variety has been built up gradually from natural mutations and genetic variations spotted in the countryside and in more recent times in the nurseries of our growers. These are then propagated from cuttings to retain their particular and desirable characteristics. Some carry their origins in their cultivar name, such as 'Kynance' from the Cornish

cove of that name.

Others introduce us to the original enthusiasts, such as 'Mrs Ronald Gray' found by her husband on the cliff edge in Devon in 1933; he has a cultivar of *Erica mackaiana* named after him.

There is already a natural range of colours on most heathlands to the eye of anyone attuned to subtle variations through the harmonies of pinks and mauves, even white if you are very lucky (primarily in Scotland). The notion of white heather being 'lucky' appears to be of 19th century origin too. An important contribution was made that century when the gardener of Sir Charles Lemon spotted a double flowered Ling, which was brought back and grown in Lemon's garden for many years. It was given the name *Calluna vulgaris flore plena* and in 1929 the Royal Horticultural Society's Award of Merit (although no longer valid since changes to the system). It is still available and has been joined by another lovely pink double named after 'J. H. Hamilton' who was at one time a partner in the Maxwell & Beale nursery. It came from Yorkshire rather than the southern heathlands but that famous

nursery did market several heathers of southern origin. From Broadstone Moor in Dorset came 'Mrs Pat' in 1925 - found by and named after the wife of the nursery manager, P. S. Patrick. In 1926 an unknown lady walking her dog in the New Forest found another fine variation and sent three cuttings to the nursery of which two rooted and so in 1928 the nursery introduced the famous 'H.E.Beale'. Their 'Mullion' came from Mullion Cove in Cornwall in 1923.

Cornish heathland has been a good source of all the heathers. Around 1929 a Miss Moseley found a tiny grey foliaged *Calluna* growing in a crevice of the serpentine rock near the Lizard. She gave it to Walter Ingwersen, founder of the famous nursery of that name, to propagate and in due course it was given the pet name of the lady's sister and marketed as 'Sister Anne'; she was, incidentally, also a nurse. That same great plantsman has 'Walter Ingwersen' named after him. He collected the original material in 1928 from the Minho Mountains of Portugal It was a' valuable addition not only for its exceptionally long lilac flower spikes but also because it extends the colour season in the garden by flowering so late. He named it 'Elegantissima' only to have that disallowed because it was already in use for a Dutch cultivar, so it was named after him instead. It did not prove fully hardy and so is now extinct, succeeded by later grey-leaved discoveries.

Cornwall also provided material for the Foxhollow Nursery, whose John F. Letts found 'Mousehole' in the Penzance area about 1965. Their good spreading cultivar, 'Foxhollow Wanderer' was found growing over one of the old Cornish copper mines.

The above are just a few of the many cultivars originating in the southern heaths, selected here because they have stood the test of time and are still available commercially. Do not, however, let the foregoing encourage you to uproot our wild plants; *Calluna* can be propagated very successfully from just one tiny cutting.

Information on the cultivars generously provided by Daphne Everett of the Heather Society.

DODDERS

Cuscuta epithymum (L.) L.
and other species

It's quite a red letter day when you find Dodder spreading over the Ling and Furze. It used to be so common it was a menace. The gauze of pink stems bobbled with tiny heads of flowers can be quite eye-catching in high summer when it's had a chance to bulk up. This is a true parasite. There are no leaves, not even 'seed leaves' or cotyledons inside its seeds. All it has in there is a minute coil of stem which bursts out when the temperature and moisture are right. It waves around to find a suitable host and then it's off. Failure to find a host stem within reach results in death so look for Dodder where the heather is a carpet of thick short juicy young shoots. It has to be quick to find a host as it has no roots to find its own moisture. Instead its roots have become modified suckers (haustoria) along its stem which it forces into the host's stem and sucks out all the food it wants. Its leaves are now nothing more than tiny scale-like bumps on the stems. Even among the world's parasites this is a very unusual plant.

Needless to say if this gets into the fields it can cause crop failure and that is exactly what it did - hence names like Hellbind, Hellweed, Red Tangle and Strangleweed. There were different Dodders for different crops, ranging from Flax to Clover and when seed was imported so foreign species came in too. In one test, early this century, a pound of Clover seeds contained 18,000 seeds of European Clover Dodder and 7,300 seeds of Chilian Dodder. This state of affairs was finally overcome with herbicides, seed dressings, and improved techniques of seed cleaning. How many different species there were is impossible to say as some species have a range of hosts but have been recorded separately. Older records, of course, predate the precise techniques used today to differentiate different species. Some appear to be extinct while the Great Dodder is rare and even the smaller European Dodder presented in this section is hard to find. It will be interesting to see which turn up in the current survey of the British Flora due for completion in the year 2000.
(For agricultural information see H.C.Long, *Weeds of Arable Land*, Min. of Agriculture and Food Bulletin 108; HMSO, 1938)

It's been around a long time. The early farmers of the Neolithic and Bronze Ages had Dodder in their crops. Now it is often on the heathlands that the European Dodder, *Cuscuta epyithymum*, finds a safe refuge. Books regularly list Furze as one of its main hosts but the botanists asked recently reported Ling almost exclusively. As for its virtues these seem to be limited to medicines and statements in the 19th century that it was *not* used in medicine are difficult to accept when famous herbals like Culpeper's and K'Eogh's had been promoting it.

The fact that its appearance was blamed on the Devil should not have barred it from medicinal use; other important medicines have come from 'satanic' herbs. Local names for Dodder have included Clover Devil, Devil's Guts, Devil's Net and Devil's Thread. The name Dodder itself has been in use since the 13th century but its meaning is lost to us; perhaps it had something to do with its frailty and thereby gave rise to 'dodderer' for a frail person.

Maybe there *was* a problem over using it in medicine since Culpeper chose his entry for Dodder as appropriate for one of his famous defenses- "*Sympathy and antipathy are two hinges upon which the whole model of physic turns; and that physician that minds them not, is like a door off from the hooks, more like to do a man mischief than to secure him.*"

One of its prime uses has been as a diuretic and therefore valued for kidney and urinary problems and their obstructions; opening the gall bladder against jaundice, and also for liver and spleen. Use too much and it's purgative, or as K'Eogh put it in his Irish herbal, "*a good cleanser*". Purging must have been an important use since this gave rise to the name of the species, *epithymum*, from the purging herb *epithumon* listed by Dioscorides (Greek; 1stC. AD). Purging the blood was considered vital, even for mental problems as highlighted by Culpeper who said Dodder was "*accounted the most effectual for melancholy diseases, and to purge black or burn choler, which is the cause of many diseases of the head and brain, and also for the trembling of the heart, faintings and swoonings.*"

Although not usually listed for feverish conditions, Culpeper lists it for agues "in children", which is unusual in itself as so rarely in the old herbals did children get special consideration let alone reduced dosages.

Lastly, it was used in both Britain and Ireland against scabies and other skin conditions. These were called the *scald,* giving rise to Dodder being called Scaldweed or simply Scald. The suggestion that these names derive from a supposed scalded appearance that Dodder gave to infected crops isn't very convincing, especially when other European names, such as the German *Grind* (scabies), refer to skin conditions too.

Although considered a noxious weed, resposible for economic loss, Cooper and Johnson reported that "*Dodder poisoning has not been reported from Britain.*" It may have gone unreported of course and some cases of poisoning may not have been linked with Dodder. In Russia it has caused chronic poisoning; horses are said to be the most susceptible. It is tempting to wonder whether Dodder was far more common when the Ling and Furze were cropped and therefore found more often in juvenile growth state that would suit the parasite. Nevertheless, no new evidence came to light for this study. We don't know whether villagers resorted to trying to rake it out; we don't know whether Dodder was one of the reasons for firing areas of heathland on occasion; we don't know whether the cowherds and shepherds kept their livestock away from infected areas. All three measures could well have been practised from time to time from place to place but there does not seem to have been widespread concern about it.

The final word goes to John Pechey whose hatred of a noxious arable weed makes it sound quite appealing! "*This fawning Parasite, and ungrateful Guest, hugs the Herb it hangs upon, with its long Threads, and reddish Twigs; and so closely embraces it, that at length it defrauds the hospitable Herb of its Nourishment, and destroys it by treacherous Embraces.*"

(*The Compleat Herbal of Physical Plants*; 1694)

BROOM

Cytisus scoparius (L) Link.

Broom waves great armfuls of golden blooms around its head like a joyous pilgrim in some grand medieval procession. It even smells a bit medieval to some people while others love the tang it puts in the air. It attracts bees which find pollen to feed upon but no nectar. Formerly it was a commonplace shrub. In the 17th century when Evelyn thought of "barren" places they were for '*Fern, Broom and Heath etc.*' (Silva, p.8) but he does not think of Furze - areas of Furze were cropped and valued rather than being barren.

Since then Broom has gone into sharp decline, due probably to loss of habitat. It likes open disturbed soil in order to germinate and then not too much competition from other plants, which are conditions in rather short supply today. Protected heathlands no longer get their soil disturbed whereas turf cutting must have been a great bonus in the past. Another advantage to the Broom must have arisen wherever the heathlands were fired to improve grazing since the seeds germinate very rapidly after a fire, giving the shrub a head start over its competitors. Although there are still fires today there's a shortage of Broom to seed into the ashes. Previously, Broom probably extended its range into field edges and the fields themselves when they were lying fallow, since it likes a slightly richer soil than Furze and other companion plants. We now know from gardening experience that the shrub doesn't like a shallow soil nor one that is very acid; indeed it will tolerated lime up to pH 6.5. Fields left fallow that had been marled would have suited it. Otherwise it

must have liked the deeper soils in the combes running off the heaths. These fringe areas with deeper better soils are the very ones that have been taken into cultivation and on to which urban development has spread, depriving the shrub of its preferred habitat.

Alternatively, Broom grows in the pools of sunlight at the edge of woodland and evidently always did, judging from the anonymous medieval *Ballad of Green Broom* which begins, "*There was an old man lived out in the wood, / And his trade was the cutting of Broom, green Broom...*" which of course does not say that the Broom was in the wood but later, *"Jonny arose and slipp'd on his clothes / and away to the wood to cut Broom."* From this ballad we also learn that the cutting was achieved with *'knives'*, which statement has been used here in the interpretative illustration.

Today Broom also finds the necessary extra nourishment beside the heathland car parks where visitors' dogs dump a deposit of nitrogen!

Broom would not have been one of the earliest of the heathland plants to colonise after the last Ice Age as it is not entirely hardy. Seedlings are killed outright by a sharp frost. It would not have crept in under cover of protective trees either since it is not shade tolerant. Today it can be found at the edges of woodland but only where the sun shines directly upon it. As the climate warmed so our ancestors became more familiar with it. There would have been more of it than today and they put it to good use. So much so that many places took their names from it. Just look at the index of a British road atlas to see how many places do begin with 'Broom' while others begin with with 'Brom' which was the Old English spelling. It's the same story in the non-Germanic parts of the British Isles, being Banadle in Wales, whether as Banhallen in the South or Banadlen in the North, while the Cornish Banathel survives as Bannel or Banathal. This reflects not only its economic value over thousands of years but also its cultural importance in the folklore and rituals of so many peoples. It has strong associations with what might well have been fertility rituals:

> Take ye the blossom of the broom,
> The blossom it smells sweet,
> And strew it at your true-love's head,
> And likawise at his feet.

(from *The Broomfield Hill* ballad, recorded by 16thC.- see Child)

Its prime use has been for making brooms (separate chapter). The dead twigs make good fuel so its charcoal has been found in a Mesolithic site well over 6,000 years old. Being a short-lived shrub there must have been plenty of dead ones to use. This use must have persisted for in the 17th century John Evelyn commented that to burn Broom took the pressure off other fuels. Otherwise it was mainly a medicinal plant although it was used in food and drink. Its leaves yield a green dye, its fibrous bark has been used for paper and cloth (although Spanish Broom, *Spartium junceum*, is used more widely) and for tanning (although again there are better options) and the twigs have been used for thatching. Very old bushes may have a trunk that even today would be desirable to the woodworkers. Apparently it's very hard and beautifully veined so it has been tried for veneers. Its hardness was exploited in the distant past for darts and spears.

POISON !

Broom is the only significant poisonous plant on the heathlands but having said that, it is not powerful in small doses and so should give no cause for alarm to visitors to the heathlands. Its tough stringy stems are not the sort of thing children are going to pick and munch as they walk along! Apart from that it tastes very bitter.

Over the centuries man has learned how to use two of the main toxins to his advantage. These active principles are scoparin and sparteine but the plant contains others such as cytisine, genistein, lupinidine, and sarothamnine, although it is thought that some of these may be synonyms for each other or else act in the same ways. Only when large amounts are used in food, drink and medicines (see below) should caution be exercised.

It's a salutary thought that in using Broom as a medicine we are taking poison! That's normal. Most medicines are toxic which is why we have such concepts as a safe dose, an overdose and reduced dosages for children. We can only get them under special 'licence' called a prescription. It's only when so much is taken as to cause adverse effects that they are thought of as poisons, otherwise it's a case of "a little does you good!"

This shows up well in the knowledge of the shepherds. They knew that Broom, especially the flowers and pods, had narcotic qualities (apparently sheep got quite drunk on the stuff), yet it was also believed that including it in sheep fodder warded off

29

the rot. John Aubrey recorded for his *Natural History of Wiltshire* (1685) that sheep suffered from rot where the Broom had been cleared and *"so ever since they doe leave a border of broome about their grounds for their sheep to browse on, to keep them sound."* Here, incidentaly, is another clue to the possibility that Broom was an arable weed on poor soils - was Aubrey's 'border' around the edge of the arable fields being left fallow? Later, another sharp observer, William Withering, believed that using the green stems as winter feed for sheep saved them from both the rot and from dropsy. It was his interest in treatments for dropsy that led to him realising the value of Foxgloves and introducing them safely into today's heart medicines.

Today Broom is unlikely to be a major problem where grazing has been re-introduced on the heathlands as there isn't likely to be enough of the shrub. It takes over 11kg to poison a horse, or so says popular tradition. It grows mixed in with other herbage and when animals have a choice they take a very varied diet. Only when unwell do they make a bee-line for particular plants that they know will heal their ills, from which much of our veterinary knowledge has derived.

BROOM IN MEDICINES

When the heathland folk needed medicines they had a powerful ally in the Broom, provided they treated it wisely. Our earliest indications of its medicinal usage date from Saxon times. Later in the Middle Ages the famous Welsh physicians of Myddfai used it and by 1618 it was in the British Pharmacopoeia although soon afterwards increased knowledge of other plants meant Broom was to some extent superseded. Sixteen preparations are listed in the 1993 British Pharmacopaeia.

Broom belongs to the legume family which includes peas and beans and makes it the second most important family for feeding the world. Broom's distinction lies in it being the only native member to become an official British drug. It was cultivated first as a medicine long before fashions in gardening started to include such shrubs for their aesthetic value. Medicinal products have included *Flores Genistae* or *Flores Scoparii* from the flowers, *Succus Scoparii* from the fresh sap; *Fluid Extract of Broom, Infusion of Broom, Decoction of Broom* and *Scoparii Cacumina* from the tops and *Sal Genistae*, from the salts in the ashes of burnt tops which were treated as lye and drunk down with a glass of wine. When the

seeds were being used the medieval physicians of Myddfai said take nine for yourself but devote the tenth to God.

There are home remedies containing Broom which are still in use today but before any reader gets enthusiastic to try some, read the section on poisons above. Broom should definitely be avoided by anyone who is pregnant due to its oxytoxic activity, and, by anyone with high blood pressure as it is hypertensive and will affect the heart and respiration. It can also upset the stomach and bowels, for which it has been exploited as an emetic and a purge. It is variable though, like most herbs, and as William Withering pointed out, can be quite drastic with one patient while having little effect upon another.

Broom

has long been taken as a diuretic, to stimulate the kidneys into removing excess fluid from the body and thereby flush out the kidneys and bladder when they had problems. The liver responds at the same time. As diuresis works it affects the lymphatic system making Broom useful for dropsy - Johnson reported that the Swedish army was cured of dropsy by it, following a fever epidemic in 1759. Gout too is cleared by the diuresis and for this Broom was used even by royal physicians, according to Gerard:- *"That woorthie Prince of famous memorie Henrie 8 King of England was woont to drinke the distilled water of Broome flowers against surfets, and diseases thereof arising."* There was the alternative of compounding the flowers into hog's lard to make an ointment for external application to painful gouty parts.

Yellow jaundice was treated with it too, in common with many other yellow flowers, since the colour was believed, according to the Doctrine of Signatures, to be an indication from God that this was His intended purpose for the plant. It must have been foul as enough flowers had to be boiled in milk to make it very bitter. It was curdled with vinegar and, if you were lucky, spiced to hide the taste. You were supposed to get half a pint of this down you first thing every morning for a week. It must have been just as bitter from those physicians who prescribed it mixed with equal amounts of Dandelion root. Easier, no doubt, were the doses of ashes of Broom, as per K'Eogh's Irish herbal: *"The ashes infused in white wine powerfully provokes urine, and are good for jaundice."* People today still have childhood memories of Broom medicine for yellow jaundice and testify to its unpleasantness.

For black jaundice (the name changes with the colour of the skin depending upon the disorder) Broom was the prime remedy:- *"Take as many handfuls (as you thinke good) of the dried leaves of Broom gathered and brayed to powder in the moneth of May, then take unto each hand full of the dried leaves one spoonful and a halfe of the seed of Broom braied into powder: mingle these together, and let the sicke drinke thereof each day a quantity first and last, untill he find he some ease. The medicine must be continued and so long used untill it be quite extinguished: for it is a disease not very suddenly cured, but must by little and little be dealt withall."*

(Fitzherbert, The Book of Husbandry; 1534)

Compounds in the Broom alter the heart rate, the tension of the blood vessels and the blood pressure. Under professional care it is useful for tachycardia and functional palpitations and even heart failure, especially when associated with low blood pressure; similarly when this causes oedema, and when patients are in shock. The way it causes small blood vessels to constrict has made it useful in cases of excessive menstruation; for women's problems, including breast tumours, it was believed there were separate Broom plants from those suitable for men's problems. So from the South West, where Broom is called Bannel in Cornish, come references to He-bannels and She-bannels just as there were He-heathers (*Calluna*) and She-heathers (*Ericas*).

The chief agent at work in these cases is the sparteine, discovered in 1851 by Stenhouse who also found that most occurred in plants growing in full sun and in early spring (May) before flowering. Such compounds can depress the heart and nervous system, to the state of paralysis but when sparteine comes under attack by acids in the body it becomes oxysparteine, useful as a heart stimulant. The ashes or sulphate salts of sparteine are now used as an antidote to some poisons including snake venom and wasp stings (and with a foreign reputation against rabies). Perhaps the heathland folk used it against their bee stings; it would have been the most effective treatment to hand.

Lastly, it is the best heathland vermifuge - for killing bodily vermin. A tablespoonful of a lotion taken on an empty stomach shifts roundworms (and probably everything else). Externally, apply oil in which crushed tops have been boiled for *"the surest medicine to kill lice of the head or body, if any."* (Culpeper)

BROOM FOR FOOD AND DRINK

Warning - The following is recorded for historical interest and would be potentially harmful to some people if they tried it today. The toxic compounds are highlighted above.

Young tops, buds, flowers, pods and seeds of the Broom have all been used in culinary ways and not just by the poor heathland people. As a delicacy they rose to the highest point of social life when Broom tops were served at the coronation of James VII of Scotland/James II of England.

Usually it was the young buds that were harvested. Gerard said they were *"to be gathered and laid in pickle or salt, which afterwards being washed or boiled are used for sallads as capers be and eaten with no less delight."* John Evelyn included them in his book of salads, the *Acetaria* of 1699, wherein he says (entry 12) *"Broom-Buds, hot and dry [to taste] retaining the virtue of Capers, esteemed to be very opening, and prevalent against the Spleen and Scurvy; and being Pickled, are sprinkled among Sallets, or eaten of themselves."* As for being good against scurvy, caused by too little vitamin C, this would have been one of the few antiscorbutic herbal treatments available on the heathlands. Scurvy was a common and nasty problem in the past and should not be thought of simply in terms of sailors nor simply as a skin disease. The full impact is quite horrendous.

The seeds when roasted have been used widely in Britain (and in France etc.) as a substitute for coffee. In 1862 Johnson described them as "no bad substitute". This usage lasted long in Scotland, where there were fewer alternative substitutes than in the south country. Down south it is to be wondered whether the heathland folk ever bothered with this when there were so many smugglers snaking their packhorses through the heather trails after dark, to supply what was otherwise too expensive - coffee, tea, brandy, lace, tobacco and so forth.

Broom is another brewing herb (gruet) added to beer for its bitterness, especially before the days of Hops. It was claimed to make it more intoxicating although by 1862 Johnson was disclaiming this saying it was merely a diuretic. Possibly it was the effect of the Broom's toxicity. With this in mind a correspondent enquired about the safety of Broom in home-made wine. The reply from the Royal Pharmaceutical Society of Great Britain was that due to reports that an infusion of the flowers affected the hearts of small mammals they felt it was unsafe to risk on humans and they could not recommend it for wine making. The action was due to the scoparin content. They added that the flowers were in use in herbal medicines, which were not under medical control. (corresp. courtesy R.J.Wain)

BINDING AND FEEDING THE SOIL

Broom does like to be beside the seaside - in hot dry dunes it simply sheds its leaves to conserve water and then they aren't even there to suffer from salt burn. (Without its leaves it makes food with its green stems.) It has been widely used for reclaiming sand dunes and those in France beside the Bay of Biscay (Les Landes) were much commented upon by the 19th century writers, together with reclamation work in Holland, as they endeavoured to promote its use in Britain. Where our southern heaths came down to the sea we preferred to leave our dunes as one of the seaside attractions. When being used deliberately as a sand stabiliser it was nurtured initially between hurdles until its long wiry roots had got a firm hold and even with so little nutrient in the sand the Broom does well - one of those plants admired by Hartlib in 1659: *"furze, broom, heath, these can hardly be so destroyed, but at length they wil up againe: for God hath given a peculiar propriety to every kinde of earth, to produce some peculiar kind of Plants, which its wil observe even to the world's end."* This shows up well today when new roads are cut through the heaths and the raw cuttings are rapidly colonised by the shrub until it's left waving its last dying tips over the heads of the burgeoning Furze that succeeds it. Being of the pea family it bear nodules of bacteria on its roots that put nitrogen compounds into the soil to feed the next species in the succession. To this end it was recommended as an enriching crop by the 'land improvers' of the 17th century. It would then yield a return as raw material for besoms - Broomfield is certainly a common field name, although we cannot be certain now how such fields were worked. Similarly, this supports the hints we get today that it was welcome on the fallow land and other barren places around the open fields system.

Broom as temporary thatch for ricks

THATCHING

Later writers cite Broom for temporary thatching, such as for ricks but obviously this was not always so, as Froissart wrote:

"He made carpenters to make houses and lodgynges of great tymber and set the houses lyke streetes and covered them with rede and brome so that it was like a lytell towne."

HORTICULTURAL MERIT

It is not surprising that such a grand and versatile shrub should have been introduced into our gardens. There are some 50 species from which to choose and another 80 or so from the very closely related genus, *Genista*, and these were certainly being introduced into gardens by the early 19th century. *Cytisus scoparius* was being used for hybridization around 1884 and from then until the 1960s many new hybrids were created. These total at least 69 but many have been misnamed over the years and are being clarified by means of the National Collection, held at the Northern Ireland Horticultural and Plant Breeding Station. Fresh breeding has started again at Boskoop in the Netherlands with a view to breeding dwarf versions for containers and patios.

1884 was the year E. André found an interesting natural variant growing wild in Normandy. It was the usual yellow except that the wing petals were of a rich brownish crimson that was echoed in the markings of the standard. It was named after him , as *Cytisus scoparius* 'Andreanus' and proved so significant as to give its name to the whole group. These range from yellow through to brown and bi-colors. In 1900, at Kew, 'Andreanus' was crossed with *Cytisus multiflorus*, the White Spanish Broom. The result had flowers of a deep rose flushed scarlet and was named *C. dallimorei* and in turn became the parent of some of the best hybrids, ranging from carmine-red, pink-red, salmon through to the whites.

A rich harvest has been derived from this one heathland shrub. Most of the work has taken place in England, (West) Germany, Ireland and Holland, with a Californian nursery working for the American market. In England the chief centre in a southern heathland setting was that of George Underwood and Son at Hookstone Green, among the other famous nurseries at Woking, Surrey (Jackman's, Goldsworth, Knaphill, etc.) Their sites had been ploughed out of the vast Woking Heath and so the soil was well suited to the Underwood's specialism in hardy heathers and Brooms. Of the latter, their introductions of lasting value include: 'Eastern Queen' (amber yellow with deep red wings), 'Eileen' (whitish yellow with pink-red wings), 'Enchantress' (pink with red stripes), 'Hookstone' (lilac standard with orange wings), 'Hookstone Purple' (uniform purple fading paler), plus 'Princess', and 'Ken Underwood'.

In the heathlands south of Woking, at Elstead, came another famous nursery in 1958; that of Albert and Arthur Burkwood with G. R. Skipwith. They were the champion plant breeders of 'Burkwoodii' fame - indeed in one of their catalogues they stated, *"We are the sole raisers of all 'Burkwoodii' hybrids and of the majority of the better Brooms and evergreen Ceonothus."* Their hybrids included 'Geoffrey Skipwith' and of more lasting fame, 'Burkwoodii' (cerise with deep crimson wings edged yellow) and 'Maria Burkwood' (red with coppery wings'). Before starting the nursery (at Kingston-upon-Thames in 1928) Arthur Burkwood (1888-1951) had worked for the Donard Nursery in Co.Down which also produced good new Brooms.

Assistance with this section was given generously by Cathal Ellis at the National Collection at the Northern Ireland Horticultural and Plant Breeding Station, Manor House, Loughgall, Armagh, BT61 8JB

References:
The Hillier Manual of Trees and Shrubs, 6th ed 1991.David and Charles.
Krüssmann, Gerd, *Manual of Cultivated Broad-leaved Trees and Shrubs*, (Trans. Michael E. Epp); 1984; Batsford
Willson, E.J.; *Nurserymen to the World*, 1989; E.J.Willson.

SUNDEWS

Drosera rotundifolia L.
Drosera intermedia Hayne
Drosera longifolia L.
and hybrids

Think small all you people who say you would like to see this insect-eating plant for yourselves but cannot find it. It's so large on a television screen whereas the Sundew can be quite tiny. A whole plant can sit in a teaspoon. It is, however, a spoonful of wonder and beauty, to which alchemists added more than a dash of magic. They knew dew came by the cool of the night and disappeared under the warming influence of the sun, and yet the Sundew plant was observed to be adorned with dew drops that persisted through the hottest sunshine. That made it very special, very magical and they pounced upon it for their experiments. These led to important liqueurs and medicines. These three themes are presented separately below but readers need to consider them together as they are so closely interrelated.

SUNDEW AND THE ALCHEMISTS

Alchemists were medieval scientists. Some were fakes with little or no skill or knowledge but some were at the other extreme and made valuable contributions to laboratory techniques and to the knowledge of chemistry, especially metallurgy. Thanks to them the world learned of sulphuric, nitric and hydrochloric acids but their results were far ranging. For example, in this book, the chapter on Bracken includes soap, glass, leather, fermented drink, potash and potassium carbonate, all of which have their histories rooted in the discoveries of the alchemists. Their findings spread widely through the civilizations: Greek, Syrian and Egyptian; East Indian and Chinese, and through the countries of Islam.

They are perhaps best known for trying to turn base metals such as lead into gold and silver. To them this seemed feasible because they believed that the nature of all matter depended upon it having a sort of soul. If that soul could be transferred from one substance to another then its characteristics would go with it. Such a transference would need an intermediary and thus they searched for the 'philosopher's stone'. Their studies led on to the search for the 'elixir of life' that would cure all illnesses and defeat death.

This is where the Sundew caught their attention. Dew was considered very special by the alchemists and the 'dew' drops on this plant defeated the sun, refusing to die as the day aged. It was not realised that this was not dew at all but globules of a viscid fluid containing enzymes capable of splitting proteins. This is produced to trap and digest insects. Their bodies provide a supplement of essential nitrogen that is otherwise deficient in the plant's heathland habitat. These fascinating aspects of the plant escaped close scrutiny at an early date simply because the Sundew is absent from the Mediterranean region where so much early medical knowledge was gained by the Arabs, Greeks and Romans. Once discovered, however, the Sundew was explored as an ingredient for the elusive elixir of life, leading to it becoming an important ingredient of a liqueur and an important medicine.

SUNDEW IN LIQUEURS

Sundew became known by the Latin *Ros Solis* or *Rosa Solis* which means simply the flower or rose of the sun. This is also the name by which the liqueur came to be known. That implies the Sundew was considered the vital ingredient but a wide range of other herbs and spices were included. Some of these were for 'magic' purposes in the search for the elixir of life but others, with strong flavours must have been to disguise the bitterness of the Sundew. Many are also very aromatic so perhaps the elixir didn't smell too good without them! Geoffrey Grigson in his *Englishman's Flora* quotes the ingredients listed by Thomas Coghan in his *Haven of Health* of 1548. The mixture contained sugar, mace, ginger, nutmeg, cinnamon, aniseed, liquorice and dates; sometimes with rose petals; or else with ale, rosemary, sage, thyme, chamomile, marjoram, mint, avens, fennel, dill, pelletory, lavender, hyssop, roses and spices. A copy of the 4th ed. of 1636 is different and reads:-

"First, because this drinke beareth the name of a certaine herbe called Rosa Solis, which is not everywhere, nor at all times to be found, it shall be necessary to speake somewhat concerning the gathering of the same. I finde by experience that it groweth most plentifully in marish grounds and fennes, and is most flourishing in June, July and August. In Lankashire in their mosse grounds where they dig their turves, there is great store of it, and there the common people doe call it youth grasse, and they think that it rotteth sheep, howesover it preserveth men. If it be gathered about noone, you shall finde upon it like as it were an oyle or dew, and if you touch it with your fingers, they will be slymy. When you would occupy it, gather it in dry weather, and about the mid time of the day, and pick it cleane from dyrt and pelfe, and cut off the rootes, or it be rancke, you may cut it hard by the roots in gathering. Now when you have prepared it in this order, and would compound Rosa Solis, take a pot of good Aqua vitæ, or Aqua composita, and put into it two good handfulls or more of the herbe called Rosa Solis, and halfe a pound of fine Sugar, halfe an ounce of whole Mace, of ginger pared, of Nutmegs, of Cinamome, of Anise seeds, all grosse beaten in a morter, of each halfe an ounce, Liquorise an ounce, first made cleane from the barke, then cut in small peeces and a little punned, Dates foure ounces, cut small, and the stones, and the white skinne that is within taken out, put all together into a large pot or bottle, and stop it close, and so let it stand for three moneths shaking it, or stirring it together now and then, afterward (if you list) you may straine away the stuffe, or let it remaine in all the yeare, and when you would occupy some of it, cast a cloth over the mouth of the bottle to keep in the spices. Some doe put in red rose leaves also in making." (transcript provided kindly by the Royal Botanic Gardens, Kew.)

Coghan was not the first to record the drink. In 1597 John Gerard first issued his *Herball* that has run into numerous editions ever since, and therein he says:-

"If any be desirous to have the said drinke let them lay the leaves of Rosa Solis in the spirit of wine, adding thereto Cinnamon, Cloves, Maces, Ginger, Nutmeg, Sugar, and a few grains of muske, suffering it to stand in a glass close stopt from the aire and set it in the Sun by the space of ten daies, then straine the same and keep it for your use."

People were indeed desirous for the drink. John Aubrey in his *Natural History of Wiltshire* (1685) noted that around Malmesbury, *"the strong-water men there do distill, and make great quantitys of it."* In 1673 he noted for his *Natural History and Antiquities of the County of Surrey* that Ros Solis *"grows plentifully"* at Walton-on-Thames, from the banks of the river across to St.George's Hill. It is difficult to imagine that area as wet open heathland for it is now completely built over! Even so, the observations on habitat in the various herbals do encourage the thought that in the past the Sundew was perhaps tolerant of a wider range than at present, so long as it was wet. The brew has changed too - the Sundew has been replaced by raisins so changing the bitterness to sweetness. This is the Italian Rossoli, also known on the Continent as Rosoglio or Rosolio.

SUNDEW IN MEDICINE

Even in Britain its restricted distribution prevented it becoming a standard ingredient in folk medicines. It was known and used in the Middle Ages by the Welsh physicians of Myddfai who, without the guidance of Classical knowledge, must have investigated the properties of this plant for themselves. The first English 'scientific' study was William Turner's *New Herball* and therein Sundew gets an entry in Part III of 1568. It is, however, conspicuous for being such a scant entry, indicating that Turner had not seen a living specimen, or else his sharp eye and scientific mind would have given him more to write than simply:-

"Rosa Solis is a little small herbe that groweth in mossey groundes and in fennes and watery mores [moors], with a brode hory [broad hoary] thinge in the toppe. It groweth not above the height of thre or foure fingers height."

Without the authority of the early Mediterranean writers Turner admits his limitations:-

"Our English men now adayes set very muche by it and holde that it is good for consumptious and swouning and faintnes of ye harte but I have no sure operience of this; nether have I red of anye olde writer what vertues it hath wherefore I dare promise nothing of it."

Honest, and correct in that the information given to him had been ascertained back in the Middle Ages by the physicians of Myddfai and has been accepted and acted upon right up to the present, for the respiratory and circulatory systems. Before considering those in more detail there are some lesser attributes of note.

Ageing is still as important to people as it was to the alchemists and even in this century Sundew was still being recommended as a 'cure' for old age in the United States Note that in Coghan's description quoted above the herbs are mixed with Aqua vitæ which in his day referred to the unrectified spirits which were the basis of the alchemists' elixir of life. It's hardly surprising then that the Sundew was considered an aphrodisiac, although Gerard refers to this in relation to cows! He reported, *"Cattell of the female kind are stirred up to lust by eating even a small quantity....because through his sharp and biting qualitie it stirreth up a desire to lust, which before was dulled, and as it were asleepe."* Its use by humans is reflected in such folk names as Youth Grass (as used by Coghan) and more frequently by Youthwort - one of the names taken by the colonists to North America where it is also known as Lustwort.

Skin problems, both clinical and cosmetic, were treated with the herb. This can be harmful. The herb contains irritants and causes dermatitis in some people. It should never be used in anything but very small doses. By Tudor times this was known to people like Gerard who warned *"The leaves stamped with salt do raise blisters, to what part of the body soever they be applied."* Similarly, for his Irish herbal of 1735 K'Eogh noted, *"If bruised with salt and laid on the skin, it raises blisters. Being corrosive, it eats away at rotten sores."* For this reason it was used widely in its European homelands for burning away warts - a usage taken to America (see Rafinesque). Although Turner knew of its use for heart conditions the herb seems to have been little used in this respect. Nevertheless, by 1892 Charles Millspaugh in America was able to write that it was *"one of the most powerful medicinal agents in our country."* Over-collection has endangered the species, in the Old World, the United States and in Canada - in such states as Wisconsin, Minnesota, and Ontario. References in the 20th century for heart and circulation treatment have been as a diuretic to reduce water levels and as a reducer of blood sugar levels, for hypertension and for hardening of the arteries.

Where the Sundew really found a place for itself in medicine was in the treatment of respiratory problems. This stems from the 'magic' of the alchemists, as explained by Gerard: *"The later Phisitians [physicians] have thought this herbe to be a rare and singular remedie for all those who be in a consumption of the lungs, and especially the distilled water thereof: for as the herbe doth keepe and hold fast the moisture and dew, and so fast, that the extreme drying heate of the sun cannot consume and waste away the same; so likewise men thought that heerwith the naturall and lively heate in mens bodies is preserved and cherished."* He also adds weight to the suggestion above, that the medicine needed so many herbs and spices because it was so foul - even the distilled water, for it had *"bin observed, that they have sooner perished that used the distilled water thereof, than those that abated from it, and have followed the right and ordinarie course of diet."*

This must have been one of the medicines that gave rise to the notion that the worse it tasted the better it worked! For hundreds of years then, Sundew has been used for asthma, bronchitis, consumption, coughs, pertussis, pthisis, pulmonary catarrh, tracheitis, and whooping cough. For some conditions this was well-founded, in that the Sundew has been found to have an antibiotic action against streptococcus and pneumococcus when the pure extract is used. When homeopathy was developed it was, by 1894, being used for consumption and whooping cough and is still so used for coughs and laryngitis etc. In orthodox western medicine the old magic still lingers on and the British Pharmacopoeia of 1993 listed 43 preparations containing Sundew, albeit with the observation that it was of "doubtful value."

SUNDEW AND LIVESTOCK

To see these tiny plants flat on the ground or snuggling down in the mosses leaves one questioning whether this could ever have been grazed by the livestock on the heaths; it's not even a tempting succulent green. Nevertheless the owners of both sheep and cattle have regarded Sundew with great misgivings. They rarely recorded the variations in symptoms that would help a present day veterinary identify the different diseases and conditions. Since the late Middle Ages fatal cattle diseases have been described collectively as the 'murrain'. In Scotland, however, they had a disease which was called 'earnach' in Gaelic and this was blamed upon the Sundew, which in turn became known as ' Lus na Fearnaich', meaning the 'Plant of the Earnach'.

The disease for sheep was known as 'red rot' and again its association with Sundew came to be viewed as suspicious. By 1862 Johnson was writing,
"There is a notion in some parts of the country that the disorder called red rot in sheep is occasioned by this plant, but its leaves are never eaten by those animals, and the complaint is the result of a miasma from the boggy ground where the Sun-dew grows."
Modern science is not too keen on miasmas so by 1980 it was thought this form of purulent dermatitis was a result of increased sensitivity to light and that the Sundew might have triggered this.

(Clements, L.O.and Weavers, E.D.; 'Dermatophilus congolensis in lambs'; Irish Veterinary Jour.; 1980; 34; 65-7)

Today livestock grazing on the southern heathlands as a conservation measure are not likely to be at risk since the Sundew is no longer generally prolific and under modern management schemes the livestock would not be kept in such poor conditions that they would need to scavenge for such meagre fodder.

Sundews are under threat and should not be removed to grow at home. They won't grow under normal conditions, requiring acidity and lack of nitrogen. So much nitrous oxide is released from vehicle exhausts to drift over the heathlands that even in the wild, in the southern counties, the future for the Sundew looks bleak.

THE *ERICA* HEATHERS

DORSET HEATH
Erica ciliaris L

BELL HEATHER
Erica cinerea L.

CROSS-LEAVED HEATH
Erica tetralix L.

CORNISH HEATH
Erica vagans L

Bell Heather

When late summer sprawls over a dry sunny bank ablaze with purple Bell Heather and hummocks of bright gold Dwarf Furze then we can enjoy the most vibrant of colour schemes occurring naturally in the landscape of today. If water gathers at the bottom then the Cross-leaved Heath is likely to grow, with its softer colour scheme, although in Dorset, South Devon and West Cornwall the damp heaths may be supporting the Dorset Heath with its spires of bright reddish pink blooms. Alternatively, walk the winds of the Lizard Peninsular to see the lilac humps of Cornish Heath. They are all so different; no wonder they make such a major contribution to British horticulture.

These belong to the genus *Erica* which has some 735 species in the world of which 90% occur in South Africa; the British Isles have four, plus a few rarities and hybrids. These are called 'Heathers' but that is a very imprecise term, including, as it does, Ling, *Calluna vulgaris*. So, from time to time, the *Ericas* have been called *heaths*, especially by gardeners. In some old herbal remedies, Bell Heather was called *She-heather* while Ling was *He-heather*, reflecting separate herbal treatments for the gender of patient. However, it is not always clear which species is being extolled, nor whether the possibility of ambiguity was even realised. The accuracy of such information must therefore be treated with particular caution. At least these plants aren't toxic.

Medicinal uses were the ones that have brought the Ericas to notice; the very name comes from the Greek 'ereiko' meaning to break, because a leaf infusion was reputed to break bladder stones. That does not seem to have been exploited much in Britain where tea has been more important: just 3-4 flowering

tops in hot water, for stomach ache, general debility, lack of appetite and lack of sleep. A much stronger brew has been used for coughs. The honey is an even better tonic, good for the heart and nerves and for nervous depression. The high mineral content makes it nutritive too. Normally the bees gather *Erica* nectar with that of other flowers; for true 'heather honey' see *Calluna*.

Other uses included bedding, brewing ale, dyes (dark green and purple), tanning and thatching but many of these uses in later times appear to have been largely restricted to Scotland, Ireland, and high English moorland, where conditions restrict the range of plants so severely. It is very difficult to find such records for the south, where the climate and soils gave rise to so many better alternatives. It is possible that back in the Middle Ages and beyond, when many of the poor were poorer and the heathlands greater, such uses were normal practice.

The main economic use is for horticulture. Many people and nurseries have contributed to this and the references made already (see Broom and Ling) to the Hookstone Green Nursery of George and Leslie Underwood, can be extended here, as an example.

Their interest in heathers arose in 1936 (the same year as they began their nursery, near Woking, Surrey) with the finding of a white *Erica cinerea* on Chobham Ridge. This was marketed subsequently as 'Hookstone White'. Among their other noteworthy cultivars of this species are 'Hookstone Lavender', 'Lady Skelton' and 'Sandpit Hill'.

Many of the heathlands in their district have wet areas, suited to *Erica tetralix*, and it was in their second year, 1937, that a man brought them an unusual apricot form which he had found and this was to be marketed as 'L. E. Underwood', named after Leslie. The next year it was the turn of George's wife, Constance, who found a bright cerise one growing near Aldershot from which she was able to pull off a stem with a few roots. This was planted out in a corner of the nursery, only to be forgotten during the war but rediscovered afterwards and named 'Con Underwood'. Their son, Ken, found what is believed to be the darkest form, in Cuckoo Valley in 1951 and that has been marketed under his name, while the bright cerise 'Daphne Underwood' commemorates his wife. Another commemoration is 'Ann Berry' who was a cousin who also worked on the nursery. 'Hookstone Pink' is a particularly fine pink set off against silvery grey foliage. It was found in 1953 on High Curley at Bagshot, Surrey. The nursery ceased to trade in 1972 but one of the daughters married John Kampa (who has an *Erica carnea* named after him) and they started the 'Conifers Nursery' nearby, still running today (*on the A319 between Chobham and West End*).

Sorting out the different cultivars through the years is a major task of the Heather Society. There are over 140 for *Erica cinerea* that are recognised in The Royal Horticultural Society's Dictionary and over 30 for *Erica tetralix*. Among the latter, early ones from the wild include 'Melbury White' from Melbury Common in North Devon and 'Pink Star' which was found in Cornwall in 1963 by John Letts. One added virtue of this species is its ability to produce good hybrids: *Erica x williamsii* when it crossed with the Cornish Heath and *Erica x watsonii* when it crossed with the Dorset Heath.

The Doset Heath, *Erica ciliaris*, has spires of bright reddish pink blooms, currently having a horticultural revival, with garden centres offering grand displays in full bloom in late summer Gardeners need to remember that this is a native of Dorset, South Devon and West Cornwall and so will not be frost hardy in the open ground in colder places. Where it is not easy to overwinter large plants under cover it is best to layer outer stems at the beginning of the season and these will be well rooted by the autumn, allowing smaller plants to be cut off and overwintered. These youngsters flower more profusely too. Mature plants tend to be short-lived.

Natural variants have been taken into cultivation of which the whites, such as 'Stoborough', 'Storbaye' and 'White Wings', are well worth considering. For a softer effect

'Wych' is creamy with a pink tinge while 'Stapehill' turns purplish. When not in flower, 'Aurea' provides yellowish leaves, while 'Egdon Heath' is greyish green and 'Corfe Castle' turns bronze in winter. There is of course a full range of the pinks and reds to choose from.

Whereas the Dorset Heath is delicate and hairy the Cornish Heath, *Erica vagans*, has firm architectural qualities and is a very fine garden plant with over thirty cultivars from which to choose. The foliage is a bold green that does not look tired in long hot summers, unless of course it is one of the colour variants, such as the golden leaved 'Valerie Proudley' which is grown for this reason rather than its unimpressive bits of white bloom. With the white ones, some people do not like the way the fading blooms turn ginger when the rest of the head is still white but whatever the colour of the blooms the ginger heads remain all winter which can be most welcome. From the Underwood's nursery came 'Hookstone Rosea'. In the wild much *Erica vagans* grows on the serpentine rocks of the Lizard and therefore tolerates magnesium which can be useful on similar garden soils.
(*Inf. on Hookstone Green Nursery courtesy Daphne Everett, The Heather Society*)

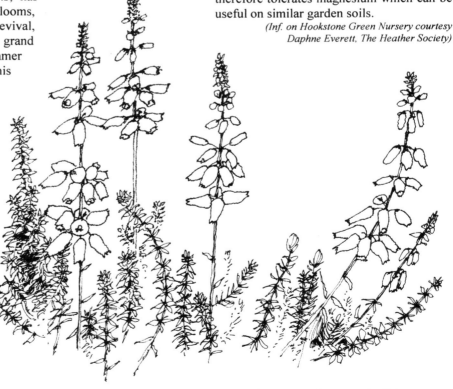

Illustrations: Top left, Erica tetralix, top right, Erica vagans, Above Erica ciliaris

BOG COTTON

COMMON COTTON GRASS
Eriophorum angustifolium Honck

HARE'S TAIL COTTON GRASS
Eriophorum vaginatum L.

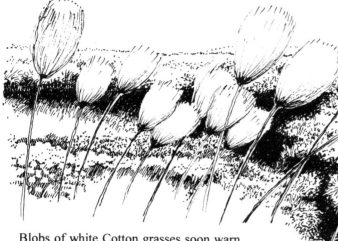

Blobs of white Cotton grasses soon warn the walker to tread warily for this is a plant of the wet areas. It does beg a closer look though, as the silky white heads wave in the winds. Even John Gerard hints that he may have picked some to take home, as he says the Cotton Grass *"of all others is the fairest and most pleasant to behold, and serveth very well for the decking and trimming up of houses, because of the beauty and braverie thereof."*

"Some charming native bog plants must not be neglected" wrote Gertrude Jekyll in her *Wall and Water Gardens* (1901), listing it with Bog Asphodel and Sundew. Rare would be the garden that could provide these with the right conditions, so they should be left alone. While the grasses are currently so fashionable for garden use they are perhaps at particular risk of being taken from the wild. Botanically speaking the Bog Cottons are not true grasses, for they belong to the Cyperaceae family rather than the Gramineae.

There are two main species to look out for: the Common Cotton Grass which has several heads per stalk and the Hare's Tail Cotton Grass which has only one. Both have the beautiful white silky bristles which are the part of the plant that our ancestors put to use. The early prehistoric peoples saw more of it than anyone since, judging by the dense layers of it found in the peat. During the Iron Age, some 2,500 years ago, the climate suddenly changed to being far wetter - so suddenly and with so much rain that the archaeologists find flooding layers with tree stools, heather and "dense tussocks of cotton grass" buried under new layers of peat (see Godwin).

The genus *Eriophorum* derives from the Greek 'erion' meaning wool, and 'phoreo' meaning to bear. That gives the clue to man's attempts to utilise it, giving rise to the name 'arctic wool'. It was tried as a substitute for cotton wool during World War II for the fibres absorb a lot of moisture. However, when our ancestors tried using it as a pillow stuffing they found this absorbency a disadvantage in the damp cottages, where the stuffing clumped together into uncomfortable damp lumps. Instead they used Thistle down for stuffing the baby's pillow and the fluffy seed heads from Greater Reedmace 'pokers' for general purposes.

The length of the fibres encouraged experiments with spinning and weaving, *"and very tolerable thread has been spun from it, but the fibres are brittle and do not bear twisting well. Still some very fine cloth has been made by a Mr. Helliwell,"* reported Johnson in 1862. He thought it *"might possibly answer well for paper"* bearing in mind that in his days the prime paper-making fibres did come from herbaceous plants, such as Flax and Hemp, instead of the wood pulp that predominates today. The fibres found one good use in the heathland districts - for making candle and lamp wicks.

In folk medicine the leaves and roots have been used against diarrhoea but only in such northern areas that there were few alternatives.

SHALLON

Gaultheria shallon Pursh

Come back for a moment to the American backwoods in 1806. It's December, and by evening rain sets in with violent winds from the south west and so it is decided to stop for the night - with the Clatsop Indians. Once settled in, an ageing woman arrives with a bowl made of light-coloured horn, in which is *"a kind of syrup, pleasant to the taste, made from a species of berry, called by the Indians shelwel; of these berries a bread is also prepared, which being boiled with roots, forms a soup."* This you are going to get, served in neat wooden trenchers, with a helping of cockles.

(from *The History of the Lewis and Clark Expedition*, 1893; ed. E.Coues; Dover reprint N.Y. 1965)

Selwel, Salal, Shalal, Shallon - these are the names used by the native Americans for a low spreading shrub that is widespread, in the right habitats, from Alaska to California. It was an important economic plant to them, both for its fruits as food and as a medicine for headaches, as it contains compounds similar to aspirin. Shallon thus became part of its botanical name, with *Gaultheria* honouring a Dr Gaultier, an important 18th century physician in Quebec.

In 1826 the great plant hunter David Douglas introduced the shrub into Britain. For horticulture it had merit - excellent evergreen ground cover, even under scattered pines, on poor sandy soil, with spikes of pinkish white flowers followed by purplish black berries. It was a fine addition to the growing number of ericaceous plants being introduced from around the world to satisfy the current

gardening fashion. Trouble is, it didn't stay in gardens. Birds took the berries out on to the heaths where it felt very much at home and its creeping habit enabled it to engulf native species and ultimately bring it into disrepute. It is so successful at this because it has formed an association with certain soil fungi which help it to feed in the poor soil and to produce auxins which sterilise the ground to ward off all competitor plants.

The problem was compounded where it had been planted in the wild areas of large estates as game cover. Not only did it provide cover, without impeding the progress of the 'beaters' on shoot days, but the berries made attractive feed for the game. This means pheasants in Britain although the shrub is sometimes called Partridge Berry, as are other American plants, some of which are related, just to confuse matters.

In 1914 it was first recorded as naturalised in Surrey on Leith Hill, where it now swamps over 50ha, and has gone on to become well established throughout the Lower Greensand areas of the county and out of the Weald into the Thames Basin. Hampshire has large areas in the New Forest. Sussex has it and it's invading the Dorset heaths alarmingly, and so on. It's causing much muttering among the heathland conservators.

On the other hand, it could be exploited, in the right place. Calls for it to be considered seriously as a crop plant for its fruit seem to have gone unheeded. As a soil stabiliser on new roadworks etc. it doesn't seem to have been considered. Sites would need to be self-contained so that its invasiveness does not become a problem and perhaps restricted to areas where the surroundings would be unfavourable, so that birds don't spread it further than intended. If it proved to be resistant to pollution it could serve in central reservations, cuttings, roundabouts etc. in the road network and would be better than *Hypericum calycinum* currently used. It has advantages over the *Hypericum* in being more shade tolerant and it doesn't look such a mess if not given regular management.

BOG BEAN
OR
BUCK BEAN

Menyanthes trifoliata L

Through four hundred years of writings this has been recognised as one of the great beauties of British wild flowers. In the 16th century John Gerard observed, "*Toward the top of the stalks standeth a bush of feather-like flowers of a white colour, dasht over slightly with a wash of carnation*" while this century E.A.Ellis wrote "*The petals are faced and fringed with little white threads that glitter like spun glass, giving the blossoms the beauty of frost crystals.*"

Sadly the Bog Bean is no longer a familiar plant, due in part to the extent of modern drainage of its wet habitat and due to the neglect of heathlands where sites have been invaded by Alder and Willow. In 18th century Ireland K'Eogh in his herbal said simply that it "*is so well known that it needs no description.*"

In England it would only have been so familiar in very wet water meadows and in the wet areas of the southern heathlands, as in the Devil's Punch Bowl of the 19th century before the spread of trees, when J.E.Morris could describe its "*deep and lonely horror....where in summer the boggy ground is starred and radiant with patches of bog asphodel and exquisite blossoms of buck bean.*"

It is one of the plants to have been longest in the service of man on the southern heathlands. It was there for the Stone Age hunters following the wild herds and indeed "*the extent and completeness*" of its fossil record is "*remarkable*" for not only is it so hardy and tough that it persisted through the interglacial periods but "*There is a clear indication that it might have survived the last glacial period in this country.*" (Godwin 313, 314) Its chief uses have been for food, drink and medicine and these have persisted longest with the peoples of long cold winters and short growing seasons that support only a limited range of alternatives; peoples such as the Swedes, Finns and Laplanders.

BOG BEAN BEER

The extremely bitter glycosides in this herb have long been exploited when brewing ale and still used after the introduction of Hops for brewing beer, especially where soils and climate didn't suit Hops. The Swedes long held to this tradition. The plant has been known as Bog Hop both sides of the Atlantic. It stopped the brew fermenting and also imparted an invigorating quality (it's been used widely for tonics). A popular recipe used two ounces of dried Bog Bean leaves as a substitute for a pound of hops - no wonder it was popular! Although this was deemed better than many substitutes it was not as good as Hops; nevertheless "*Large quantities are said to be annually collected for the adulteration of beer in this country; an application of the herb that must be considered fraudulent, as well as illegal, though, the plant being merely a tonic bitter, its admixture is far less injurious than many to which our national beverage is too frequently subjected.*" (Johnson 1862)

BOG BEAN BREAD

Bog Bean creeps through its wet terrain by means of fat rhizomes which are designed to float and these have been harvested (supposedly since prehistoric times) to be used for making bread. They must first be dried and powdered and then thoroughly washed to leach out the harmful bitter compounds. Apparently this was not entirely successful since the Swedish botanist Linnaeus, when recording the use, was unable to recommend it, due to its bitterness. However, Johnson said only that it was "*not very palatable, but possessed of considerable nutritious properties.*" It was an expedient for hard times, known as *missen* or famine bread to the Finns and Laplanders.

BUCKS, BOGS AND BEANS

Bog Bean was an 18th century descriptive change from Buck Bean but the reason for Buck is arguable. It came into English in 1578 with Henry Lyte's *A Niewe Herball, or Historie of Plantes* which was his translation (from a French edition) of the Dutch *Cruydeboeck* (1554) by the Flemish botanist Rembert Dodoens. Therein it was *Boksboonen* - Goat's Beans, referring perhaps to it providing animal fodder since the fruits and seeds do not resemble beans in the slightest, but the leaves do. The trefoil leaves are exactly like Broad Beans which were formerly a staple food and familiar to everyone; hence such folk names as Bean Trefoil, Bitter Trefoil, Bog Trefoil, Marsh Clover, Marsh Trefoil or Trifoil, Threefore, Trefold, Water Shamrock, Water Trefoil and the *trifoliata* of the botanical name.

Alternatively, there is the possibility that the Flemish *Bocks Boonen* has the same origins as the German *Bocksbohnen*. That could be a contraction of *Scharbocksbohnen* meaning Scurvy Beans, for the German *Scharbock* relates to the Latin *scorbutus* for scurvy. The scurvy connection is found in other European cultures including the Swedish and German, which adds weight to this option. The herb is a source of vitamin C and has long been used against scurvy whereas no record could be traced for this study concerning goat fodder; only that sheep and cattle avoid it. The name of the genus, *Menyanthes* also reflects medicinal use for that was taken from the Greek, meaning flower of the month, referring to its use for menstrual problems.

CAUTION! POWERFUL MEDICINE

This is one of the most powerful medicinal plants on the heathlands and is still employed today, but if consumed in excess can have drastic action:-
"Large doses of the root of this plant cause profuse

vomiting and purging, together with exhausting diaphoresis [sweating]. Smaller doses cause confusion and vertigo, pressive headaches, dimness of vision, contraction of the pupil, twitching of the facial muscles, a sensation of coldness in the stomach and oesophagus, followed by nausea, distension and fulness of the abdomen, with griping, constipation, frequent desire to urine with scanty discharge, oppression of the chest with increased respiration and accelerated pulse, cramps in the legs, sleeplessness, coldness of the extremities, followed by fever without thirst, and extreme weakness of the whole body." (Millspaugh)

With over twenty main applications this is one of those panaceas for all ills, from the times of such ancients as Dioscorides and Galen up to the present when it is in preparations for psychiatric disorders and certain cancer treatments. It has been much used for the digestive system, as a tonic, for it stimulates gastric and biliary secretions to promote good digestion; also for rheumatoid arthritis resulting from digestive debility. Some dyspepsia recipes include Wormwood, Centaury and Sage. It also shifts worms. One recipe, for acute gastrodynia, recorded from medieval Wales, was well suited to the heathlands:

"Take buckbean and powder well. Also burn a quantity of gorse or broom seed in an iron pot, and reduce to a fine powder. Pour a gallon of strong old mead upon the ingredients, then cover it up well and boil, and let it stand covered until cold. You should then drink as much thereof as you may require, night and morning fasting; at other times you should drink nothing but water until you have recovered your health." (Hoffman 36)

Ultimately, small doses are laxative; it should never be used for diarrhoea. In the blood stream it is a purifier as it stimulates the kidneys and liver and so has been used for everything from jaundice to gout. By opening the pores and promoting sweating it has been a febrifuge for treating both remittent and intermittent fevers and at the same time heals skin conditions. It affects the respiratory system too, used against coughs and colds and tuberculosis (both pulmonary and scrofula).

UNEXPECTED SURPRISE

During the research for this study attention was drawn to a report of the ethnobotany of the Menomini peoples of North America who tattoo this and other herbs into their flesh for protection:-

"Tattooing was not employed by the Menomini so much for the design as for the treatment of diseases, being a talisman against their return.....The medicines were moistened and tattooed into the flesh with the teeth of the gar pike, dipped in the medicines. The various colors stay and form a guard against the disease. After the tattooing is done, the surface is poulticed and painted with medicines."
(Smith, Huron H.; *The Ethnobotany of the Menomini*; Bull. Pub. Mus. Milwaukee 4; 1-82; 1923)

Reading this brought to mind those reports from the Romans that when they arrived in Britain they were confronted by tattooed natives. The truthfulness of these reports has been doubted and much debated but the above raises the possibility that the British may have tattooed themselves as a safeguard against the invaders Additionally, in recent years a deep-frozen prehistoric body has been recovered on the Continent and that was tattooed, so at least we can be certain that the technique was in existence.

Where it was wet enough for the Bog Bean it was good feeding for Curlews, as on Thursley Heath today. People used to take the eggs for food.

SWEET GALE

OR

BOG MYRTLE

Myrica gale L.

Some of the least noticeable plants have proved to be the most virtuous. The Sweet Gale is one of them.

Gale has been one of the great serve-alls of the humble cottagers. They could make beer with it or flavour food, get medicines or dyes, repel moths from the linen drawers or mosquitoes from the bedloft, drive out stale smells by treading it into the floor or by burning it.

Down where it's wet and soggy, beside pools, along streamsides or just generally boggy, is where this low shrub likes to grow. It wouldn't have been familiar to the cottagers of the dry heaths.

SCENTS AND BUGS

Picture if you will, sprays of the green willow-like leaves being swished around in hot water (sometimes salty) and notice the pale scum floating on the surface that will be skimmed off and saved. This is wax from the only wax producing plant of the heaths and the only one that could be described as an aromatic. It is sometimes called Bog Myrtle because the aroma reminds people of the true Myrtle, *Myrtus communis*. The scent pervades the wax and the room when it is burned in candles. The trouble is, great armfuls of the shrub would need to be so treated if ever enough wax was to be warmed off the undersides of the leaves to make even one candle, so was this ever done? Leland writing of Lincolnshire in the 1530s said it was "*swete in burning*" which is not saying people went to the trouble to make candles; more likely it was strewn on the fire as an air freshener, to scent the room and drive out insects. All the same, writer after writer repeats the notion of candles. It was Johnson in 1862 who more convincingly declared it was "*not economic to grow or to gather from the wild for this purpose.*" Apparently a few found it worthwhile in Scotland for Herbert Edlin to record it in his *Woodland Crafts In Britain*. Mostly he wrote from personal knowledge. Perhaps the wax

was removed before the foliage was used in brewing and it thereby became valued as a by-product, with perhaps small amounts being added to beeswax or tallow to provide scent, without having to make whole candles from it - the smell from burning plain tallow would not please modern noses! The value put upon such air fresheners, whether special candles or herbs strewn in the fire, is probably under-appreciated today. It is easy to imagine little thought would be given to such niceties. Perhaps they were not mere niceties in all households, for even in the absence of knowledge of germs as such, our ancestors *did* associate bad smells with dirt, disease and death. Repercussions were blamed on evil forces, so certain herbs were burned to provide 'holy' smoke to drive out the smell and the evil. These ranged from sweeteners to fumigants to incense in church. Anyone trying this with Gale should use wet leaves, to get smoke and to dampen the tendency of the aromatic oils to go up with a whoosh!

The great advantage with using Gale lay in the whole plant being insect repellent, ensuring a mosquito-free night's sleep. If the herb was strewn in the bed then it could be a flea-free night's sleep too! Every household had fleas. Remember how fast the Black Death spread. For severe infestations the bedding, clothing etc. could be drenched with a strong decoction of the herb. Sprigs of it were strewn in clothing chests and linen drawers etc. which served to keep out the clothes moth too. Thus in 1791 William Lewis reported of it: "*The leaves are said to be used by the common people for destroying moths, and cutaneous insects, being accounted an enemy to insects of every kind.*"

(*An Experimental History of the Materia Medica*; 4th ed. ed.by [and improved] John Aitken; London).

In Surrey it can be found growing today in Lightwater Country Park, down by the ponds, where it has been since before 1692 when John Aubrey recorded it: "*at Light-Water-Moor, grows great Store of a Plant, about a foot and a half high, call'd by the Inhabitants Gole, but the true Name is Gale.....it grows also in several Places of this healthy Country, and is used to be put in their Chests among their Linnen, Etc.*"

(*Natural History and Antiquities of the County of Surrey*)

In 1994 a television news item announced that the absence of midges wherever Gale grew on the Isle of Skye was being investigated scientifically as a possible source of commercial insect repellent. Local people collected the Gale and the oil was extracted by steam distillation and proved effective so that in 1995 it was marketed, under the trade name 'Myrica'. The recent revival of interest in chandling as a leisure pursuit has also brought fresh attention to the shrub and it is said to be included in some brands of 'scented sachets'.

GALE BEER

Gruets or brewing herbs were used as a mixture in the old recipes, rather than simply the Hops of today, but it was the Gale content that was so prized as to give its name to Gale Beer. This was not just for flavour and aroma but in the belief it made the brew more intoxicating. William Turner, reported cheerily, *"It is tried by experience that it is good to be put in beer both by me and by divers others in Somerset."*

[spelling modernised; *A New Herball*, Part III (1568)]

This is presumably Turner as the 'Father of English Botany' rather than in his other role as Dean of Wells Cathedral! In Gerard's Herbal we can't tell from the wording whether he was approving when observing it *"was fit to make a man quickly drunke"* but by 1791 William Lewis was definitely dampening when he noted it *"as a substitute for hops for preserving malt liquors, which they render more inebriating and of consequence less salubrious."*

Waverley Abbey, Surrey - ruins of possible cellarer's room.

The usage was ancient and of importance throughout Northern Europe where, in places, the plant was given legal protection. It's fame in Sweden spread to America. In Britain it is said to have declined after the 14th century. There would certainly have been a decline in the 16th century with the closing of the monasteries and their brew-houses. Many a monastery had its own favoured recipe. Some were similar to today's with Gale instead of Hops being added to malt, yeast, water and sugar, although this was an expensive recipe, perhaps reserved for the Abbot, since sugar was not available cheaply. More usually the sweetening came from Angelica. Other gruets included Dandelion flowers, Elder berries, Ground Ivy, Heather, Mugwort, Nettles, Tansy, and Yarrow. This must have been a very bitter brew so presumably large amounts of Angelica were needed to counteract herbs like Tansy, Mugwort and Yarrow. Another popular gruet was 'Bog Rosemary' but several plants have borne that name. The Royal Horticultural Society suggested this was either *Andromeda polifolia* or *Ledum palustre* and in this context prefer the former; it is no longer common enough on the southern heaths but its distribution is known to have been far wider in the past.

In the monasteries it was the sub-cellarer's task to organise the brewing. This was on a large scale, as ale was used as part-payment for servants, and was served each day to everyone in the monastery including guests and most of those servings had to be of good quality - *"never withe newe ale, nor palled or over sowre."* Although monasteries varied, a typical weekly allowance per person in the later Middle Ages was seven gallons - four of good ale and three of weaker. That was equally true of nunneries. Water was served only out of necessity or as a punishment to mortify the flesh.

Gale declined rapidly in the south with the rise in Hops as both a bitter flavouring and as a preservative, because Hops could be grown as a crop. Where Hops couldn't be cropped well, Gale lasted until the 18th century and much later in some isolated parts of Yorks, Lancs, Scotland, etc. Today there is a revived interest in old ales and beers and their gruets, including Gale.

PECULIARITIES

This is a very odd plant. Science cannot be sure exactly what it contains; a 1974 analysis produced results markedly different from those published earlier and totalling 41 different compounds. It may be that there are differing strains of the plant, implying that what is a safe usage in one district may not be so safe in another. In particular it is noted that a number of recipes, both medicinal and culinary, have been introduced into the British literature from a Chinese origin and that in China there is a definite subspecies of the plant, so these in particular should be treated with caution. The compounds include alkaloids based on nitrogen, giving it the aroma and being blamed for tainting milk - but the plant grows in soils that are highly deficient in nitrogen. It overcomes this by having nodules of bacteria on its roots which take nitrogen out of the air and convert it into solid nitrogen compounds upon which the plant feeds. This is something reserved in many people's minds as exclusive to the legumes (pea family) but there are a few other plants in Britain that have developed this association, including Alder trees and Gale.

The variability of the plant shows up so clearly in one particular oddity. It is the only British plant that doesn't know what sex to be. One year it can be male whereas the next year the same plant can be female and sometimes it can be both at the same time with a mixture of catkins.

FOOD AND MEDICINE

Owing to the variability highlighted above, Gale should be treated with caution. Some nitrogen compounds can be very harmful and in this case may be responsible for the supposed narcotic effect that induces drunkenness. Its powerful effect to the head has been exploited to advantage. From about 1475 comes the Icelandic medical MS of Thorlief Bjornsson which reflected European knowledge of that time and therein we learn of Gale that "*Its fragrance counteracts shooting pains in the head. Sweet gale crushed dries boils. The juice of sweet gale dries matter in the ears and kills their worms...*" (*Trans.* Larson 1931) He also records using green tops crushed in sour wine being applied to the head as a treatment for headaches and he said it strengthened the hair. Other people have used it for hysteria and palsies.

Bjornsson also listed it for purgation and therewith comes the indication that Gale can be toxic. A weak herbal tea has been used to settle stomach upsets but as so often happens, a little does you good but too much gives you the works and in this case Gale will cause you to vomit. It has long been known as an emetic, both sides of the Atlantic, and was getting into print at the turn of the 19th century. J. Evans went on *A Tour Through Part of North Wales in the Year 1798 and at other Times* (pub. London, 1800) and there he found the plant being called 'Bwrle' - emetic.

Our ancestors were more attuned to the natural world than we are today and we would be wise to notice they reserved this plant for minor uses in the kitchen, using the dried leaves and fruits as a garnish or sparingly in soups and stews. If we look in the literature from North America where the native peoples retained their traditions far longer, then again we find the same avoidance. In French Canada it was known (1749) as *Poivrier* - pepper, just as it was used as a spice in France itself. Medicinally it is best kept on the outside - to kill fleas, scabies, the itch and such like.

N.B. This plant should *not* be consumed during pregnancy.

Gale bark is said to have been used for tanning calf-skin. There is an Irish belief that it was once a forest tree but was cursed into its present lowly status by God as a punishment for providing the timber for Christ's Cross. In English heathland districts this belief is associated with the Elder (the Aspen in Scotland). Similarly, some Irish have avoided using Gale stems as livestock goads in the belief that these were the rods used by the Romans to scourge Christ. In pre-Christian times it may have had fertility associations and these still persist with its use in wedding bouquets.

BOG ASPHODEL

Narthecium ossifragum L.

Some of the most beautiful plants bear some of the worst reputations and that is just the case with the Bog Asphodel. From little Iris-like plants rise the flowering spikes, from a few centimetres to half way up your shins, and bear exquisite bright gold flowers. These are enhanced with contrasting orange dots which upon inspection prove to be the anthers. Even closer inspection reveals that the petal surface has a texture like flannel, to trap rain drops. As the flowers fill with water it carries the pollen grains up to the level of the stigmas, for self-pollination.

Its striking beauty, gold in flower and orange in fruit, against the darkness of the other bog vegetation, earned it the name Asphodel - the Lily of the Fields, the Elysian Fields of Greek mythology. Similarly, *Narthecium* derives from the Greek 'narthis' or little rod, after the hollow-stemmed plant in which Prometheus brought fire from the gods to earth. It may be beautiful when in bloom but its practical usefulness is very limited. The bad reputation concerns possible toxic effects upon grazing livestock. It does contain powerful saponins but there is no agreement as to whether these could be responsible for the disabling conditions associated with the plant. In particular it was believed to cause fragile bones which is the meaning of its botanical name *ossifragum*, given it by Linnaeus in the 18th century. Similarly, one of the English names for the plant is Bonebreaker while in Donegal it is Cruppany Grass since it was associated with a condition of stiff joints called cruppany. Many today think these were cases of mineral deficiency diseases, such as the 'staggers', caused by calcium deficiency and certainly the Asphodel chooses to grow in some of the most acid conditions.

Then, came a fresh crop of suspicions from a different list of symptoms, which were rare until the 1950s. They were first described by the Norwegians who named the disease Alved which means 'elf fire' but there are local British names from its occurrences

here, such as 'plotchteach' in Perthshire, 'yellowses' and 'head greet' in other parts of Scotland and 'saut' in Cumbria, but the effects have been recorded right down to Dartmoor. There are many variations between the reports but nevertheless grazing upon Bog Asphodel has been held to be the main factor.

One report suggested that the toxins could be passed on through affected cow's milk, so there are far-reaching implications. In 1989 suspicions were put to the test in a controlled feeding test and this beautiful plant is indeed highly toxic to cattle.

[see *Veterinary Record; August 1st 1992, pp.100-3*]

Obviously this is of concern today where grazing is being tried as a sustainable resource for reclaiming and conserving the southern heathlands. Fortunately the risk is reduced by the plant's natural distribution which does not include some of the southern counties. As the experimental grazing sites are fenced it is possible to select areas safe from this plant.

Maybe the plant's absence in some counties is due to man having harvested it to extinction or having eradicated it for livestock protection. Harvesting must have been quite limited. In the 17th century John Evelyn recorded that yellow hair was highly fashionable and from this time come reports that the women of Lancashire were taking the plant to provide this yellow hair dye. However, in the south there were alternatives, especially the Walnut which was grown extensively and from which a yellow hair dye could be obtained. In Shetland the Bog Asphodel was used as a substitute for Saffron, both as a dye and a medicine, but on Shetland there are few alternatives and Saffron would have been a very expensive import from the mainland, whereas in the south Calendular Marigolds were used to adulterate Saffron. Medicinally, the Bog Asphodel is calming, in an anti-spasmodic way, but is presumably too bitter for this to be a popular medicine. It has been tried for menstrual obstructions and for reducing scrofulus glands.

SCOTS PINE

Pinus sylvestris L.

When the wolves howled around the lambing folds on icy nights and the bears lurked in the heathery shadows then early farmers needed all their wits and courage to protect family and livestock. These were among the beasts of southern England right up to early Saxon times when bears are thought to have become extinct. Men had long since learned that fire filled beasts with fear. What would blaze brighter than dried pine branches? Did the farmers heap such branches round the livestock enclosures ready to ignite during wolf raids?

When the long cold winters dragged on beyond the food stores early man knew that grinding off the inner bark from Scots Pines yielded a kind of flour that proved sustaining when cooked and eaten.

The prehistoric smiths had learned the technology of making charcoal and exploiting its advantages for working metals. In so doing they discovered by-products such as pitch and learned to use that too and also that pine trees both charred well and yielded plenty of tar and pitch.

Perhaps these three important uses were responsible for the demise of the Scots Pine, for the tree disappears from the records for hundreds of years. The bread meal was a Continental usage for which no British counterpart was found for this study but that is not to say it was not used, especially as there was so much interaction with the Continent. If the trees were felled for bark stripping then it's hardly surprising the tree went into sharp decline.

One way or another the pines disappeared from the south. They had been there a long time. Various branches of archaeological science have taught us that after the last Ice Age birch trees crept into the thawing lands over the 'land bridge' (that was later breached by the sea to create the English Channel) and established Birch woods over most, if not all, of southern England, some 10,000 years ago. Then, about 9,000 years ago, the birches were displaced by advances of pines across the bridge. These may have included additional species to *Pinus sylvestris* but indisputable evidence was not known to Godwin when he wrote his *History of the British Flora*. As the climate became drier so the pines came to dominate, say 7,000 years ago, and then that phase waned in favour of a wetter warmer period which favoured deciduous trees, such as Alder, Oak, Elm and Lime. The days of the great pine forests in the south were over although the species managed to survive into the time of man.

Then they vanish so completely from the records that some claim they became extinct, until introduced again in the 17th century. That is not proven and is doubted by many. Come the 17th century and the tree starts to get recorded again but this time in relation to parks and gardens where evergreens had become highly fashionable. The Scots Pine was hardy, commercially available and cheaper than many imported exotics. Thus in all probability the tree arrived at many southern sites at about the same time. Nevertheless, the 'blame' for reintroducing it is often made to fall upon the shoulders of one man - John Evelyn. This needs closer scrutiny. Although he was an influential member of society, garden designer, and wrote the first great book on trees in Britain (*Silva: or, a Discourse of Forest-Trees*) it can be argued that he did not have a particular enthusiasm for the tree. In his *Silva* he is no more effusive for Scots Pines than some other trees, noting that for ornamental purposes they "*create a perpetual spring*" but on the whole he keeps to practicalities, saying for example, that firs and pines "*make stately, noble and very beautiful Skreens and Fences to protect Oranges, Myrtles and other curious Greens, from the Scorching of the Sun, and ruffling Winds.*" This did not inspire many plantings of pinetums to protect the tender exotics; the British preferred the less risky architectural orangeries instead. He noted that pine plantations "*exceedingly improve the Air, by their Odoriferous and balsamical emissions*" which led to him writing a separate treatise to promote the encircling of London with aromatic trees and shrubs to kill the stench but this notion was not taken up.

A second explanation for the return of the Scots Pine centres upon Sir Edward Zouch, who, as a court favourite of James I, was made keeper of the Royal Park of Woking. It is said that he planted pines in the Park to make his Scottish sovereign feel at home during his visits. It is not clear where this story comes from but it does not seem to be very old. Even if founded upon fact, the pines would not have matured and seeded through the southern heathlands at the rate at which they appear in the records. There must have been many centres from which seed emanated.

By the end of the 18th century Scots Pines were popular for plantations, where landowners turned their heathlands over to economic productivity. By the early 19th century these were ready for harvesting and of course by then were seeding prolifically into the wind. These germinated on those lands still remaining as heaths so that pines became a familiar sight. They matured majestically, hence so many places having their clump of "Cathedral Pines" or some similar image from the Gothic/Romantic Movements. Walkers could tread the quiet needled floors between the colonnaded trunks, gaze up through the rib vaulted darkness, to windows of sunbeams spotlighting the contention between Creation and Evolution.

Some pines will always be kept as they help efforts to conserve the hobby - a bird of prey that takes over the nests of crows and magpies which are themselves built in the pines. The hobby has such incredible skills that it catches swallows and dragonflies in flight - a wonderful heathland sight.

After the Second World War the government policy, through the founding of the Forestry Commission, was to increase home production of timber, especially softwoods, which resulted in mass plantings of conifers. Self-seeding became even more effective since forestry research had selected strains that flourish particularly well on such sites. Add natural selection to this and some strains are now bearing cones as early as their fifth year, even though they may be stunted knee-high strugglers. Pulling up pine seedlings has become a regular community activity in aid of conservation.

Examples of these post-war plantations are still thick on the ground but to draw upon one - Surrey County Council owned 840 acres of the Wisley/Ockham/Chatley Heaths which were planted up with Scots Pine and (unexpectedly) Lodgepole Pine, *Pinus contorta var. latifolia* Wats. These are now being removed in selected areas as part of the County's heathland reclamation scheme (and the heathland is indeed regenerating on the sites and attracting back rare wildlife - from nesting Wood Larks to Silver-studded Blue butterflies and the Sand Lizard has been reintroduced, successfully). Marginal areas will be left for amenity value as so many people enjoy walking between the tall stately trunks. These same pines enrich the local wildlife, as when they attract flocks of Crossbills, which benefit from the adjacent pond - seed-eaters have a dry diet and need water. Thirdly the pines provide a protective barrier from roads since the M25/A3 interchange now divides the site into quarters. (Public car park off the M25 slip road south, signed A3 Guildford and Portsmouth).

BRACKEN

Pteridium aquilinum (L) Kuhn

The plant has been here for over two million years, while its ancestral forms contribute to fossil records going right back to the Oligocene stage of the Tertiary period. Today it is widely dispersed from the Arctic Circle right down into the southern hemisphere, where, for example, South Africa suffers the same problems as Britain. Its uses are therefore of great antiquity but out of this long association with man only those activities likely to have a bearing upon the heathlands are explored here.

There is scarcely another British herbaceous plant that's been of such economic importance, in such a diversity of ways, as the Bracken. At the same time it has been cursed as an invasive weed. The total coverage is estimated at 6720 square km. Now it's economic potential is being studied afresh.

It has become so prolific in recent times because it has ceased to be harvested as a valuable resource. Additionally, it likes current climatic conditions: the frost-free growing season is now longer, the overall temperatures are higher, the light intensity has increased slightly to aid its photosynthesis, it likes the conditions created by acid rain which at the same time has an adverse effect upon some plants which would otherwise be the Bracken's competitors, there is less grazing and therefore less trampling of the emerging fronds, there is less deliberate burning of the heathlands to encourage grass or heather, so giving the spores a better chance to develop. The last point is somewhat double edged, for if the spores arrive immediately after fires they find the ashes rich in nutrients to aid their development, while the deep rhizomes of mature plants can escape destruction by fire and flourish in the absence of their less fortunate competitors.

Despite its tough stems and tenacious habit the Bracken is quite sensitive. It is really a woodland plant but makes advances out onto heathlands under favourable conditions or else persists after tree cover has been cleared. It is variable however; so that in Holland, for example, it does not spread out from under the trees onto the heaths in the way that it will in Britain. No doubt the more maritime climate here helps to explain that. Exposed sites leave it vulnerable to late frosts which cut back its fronds and this, or regular cutting, can weaken the plant to death. Cutting it three or four times a year for three years is said to eradicate it but it doesn't always prove to be quite that simple! Nevertheless, to conserve this renewable and valuable resource, there were restrictions over its harvesting. Regulations delayed the start of the main cutting season until the plant was at its least vulnerable - when it was mature in high summer. Thus it was usually August (the last Monday in parts of Surrey) before families with cutting rights could go out and mark their claim. This was announced in the manorial courts or, in the days of literacy, notices were pinned up around the villages. Each family then cut a swathe around the patch of bracken that was theirs by tradition. Then it was left for an agreed period, usually a week, to see if there were any counterclaims. Often there were and people still remember it causing intense strife with the neighbours.

The mature fronds were cut some time from early September through to the end of October. Then it had to be dried. Sometimes it was left spread in the open air to dry like hay. Alternatively it was stacked green, either on site or after being carted back home. Green stacks or 'bracken-cocks' were large enough (two cart loads) to ensure plenty of heat built up inside to help dry it out. This would have destroyed some of the Bracken's toxins but not all of them. Precise details of treatment vary from one location to another, reflecting local tradition entrenched in hundreds of years of the manorial system. Differences also arose from the intended purposes of the final material; stacking it green caused the heap to heat up by the same biological processes as exploited in a garden compost heap, which was beneficial when the Bracken was actually intended for compost but when it was for thatching then the heat caused it to degrade. There's a lot more to learn about Bracken.

BEDDING

Bracken has been used as bedding for both man and beast since prehistoric times. Roman usage was found in Northumberland when *Vindolanda* was being excavated while from the Viking period, a 10th century pit yielded Bracken, clover and grass which was interpreted as the stuffing from one of their mattresses, and so the records continue until present times. These are not just for bedding as we know it but could include usage as a 'strewing herb' on the floor in the days when people slept around the central hearth. Strewing Bracken was not specific to the poorer homesteads with earth floors, as from 1440 comes an observation by Palladius that timber floors of Maple, Oak and Ash would endure well if strewn thickly with fern. Such wooden floors of superior timbers were not for the poor. However, it is with the poorer homes that such usage is most often associated. Records of their sleeping arrangements are understandably rare but in 1792 Sir J. Sinclair, in *The Statistical Account of Scotland, 2* recorded that Perthshire tenants *"had no such things as beds. They lay on the ground with a little heather, or fern under them."* It is believed that the poorest people of the southern heaths continued this way until the end of the 19th century.

Livestock has always been bedded on Bracken. In terms of quantity this was one of its more important uses. Apart from the fact that many people could get it free, it was more absorbent than straw which was often needed for other uses and was limited to the amount of cereal grown in the district. The early Irish were primarily pastoralists and therefore had a shortage of straw and this applied to some of the British regions too. The fern was cut and dried at the end of the season so harvesters took it unwittingly when it had the lowest levels of toxins. Some of these toxic compounds can be passed on through the milk, which our ancestors seem to have understood, as country lore decreed that green Bracken should not be given to cows in lactation.

Buildings have also been bedded on Bracken, in days before solid foundations became normal, or else Bracken was used in conjunction with timbers laid for the purpose. Thus when the archaeologists excavated a hall of the mid-Saxon period, at Treasury Green, Westminster, they found a timber foundation raft bedded on the fern.

(Green, H. in *Illustrated London News* 29-6-1963)

Similarly roads not only had their ruts filled with the stuff but they too could be bedded upon it. From the village of Limpsfield in Surrey, come memories that when the High Street was first given a hard surface earlier this century it was laid upon a bed of Bracken six feet thick. That, it is claimed, is the reason why the road has never had to be rebuilt.

[oral tradition unsubstantiated]

COMPOST

Returning fertility to the soil by way of organic matter is a practice much older than many people think. It dates right back to prehistoric times. The Neolithic farmers, who have so often been credited with helping to create the southern heaths through their lack of understanding of good soil management, are now believed to have used Bracken compost. This has also been forwarded as an explanation for some of the finds made by archaeologists on Skara Brae, Orkney. By medieval times Bracken compost was held in high esteem. There was even a novel way of shredding it, for the 13th century treatise known as the *Seneschauncy* says straw and fern *"ought to be gathered and thrown on roads and lanes in order to make compost."*

There seem to have been three ways of using it. One was to spread it as a surface mulch - *"brakes cast upon the Ground, in the Beginning of Winter, will make it very fruitfull,"* wrote Francis Bacon, in 1627. Secondly, it could be stacked (with unwanted thistles, docks and other noxious weeds that need killing with the heat that builds up in the stack) and left with earth heaped over until it had degraded; (this persisted into living memory). Then it was ploughed in for general soil improvement. Thirdly, it could be used in a more concentrated way by adding it to the planting holes and furrows. In this respect it was regarded as being especially beneficial for Potatoes as indeed it would have been, as its high potash content promotes good roots and Potatoes enjoy plenty of bulky organic, moisture-retaining material. On alkaline soils such Bracken compost helps reduce the soil alkalinity to the level preferred by potatoes (pH 5.0-6.0) and in so doing reduces the risk of potato scab disease.

Bracken compost fell from favour in more technological times for not being a balanced fertilizer. Although it was rich in potash it was deficient in nitrogen. That, however, is not a problem in the modern nursery trade where the young stock is watered with a balance of nutrients and the compost is viewed more as a 'growing medium'. Peat has become the universal growing medium and is used much more than soil-based composts, being especially important for all plants requiring an acid medium, such as conifers and 'ericaceous' plants such as Heathers, Rhododendrons and Azaleas.

Peat is used in such vast quantities that now there is concern that extraction from the peat bogs is causing excessive destruction of this rare and precious habitat. The annual demand for peat has been running at three million cubic metres a year, necessitating imports, mainly from the Baltic region. Of this total,

horticulture takes some 30% of which 40% comes from our own bogs, reducing these wetlands down to our last 6%.

The search for an alternative medium has brought coir into use. It's made from coconut waste and its use commercially has been seen as an economic aid to some developing countries. At first it was unpopular because growers treated it in the same way as peat only to discover there are differences, especially when it comes to the watering regime. Now that these are being understood coir is increasing in popularity. It does not suit every species and cultivar but then neither does peat. Now Bracken is being tried and proving successful - more so with some species than with others of course.

Success depends so often upon the level of alkalinity required: peat is acid while coir can be alkaline (pH range 5.6-7.4) and Bracken falls between the two (usually pH 5.5-6.5 but can be 4.8). Mixing Bracken with other media is proving worthwhile; 50% suits a wide range of plants but above 75% can retard development of some others. Since 1992 the largest field trials in Britain have been undertaken by Dr. Rona Pitman for divisions of the Forestry Commission, at Fritham, Hants. Six different treatments were worked to seek the best method of composting and the resulting products were then evaluated by Efford Horticultural Research. Both July and September-cut material was tried and the latter proved the best by far, not having such a high water content and because the toxic compounds degraded away by the following spring to leave a safe product. Separate work on July-cut material has been performed at West Heath in Sussex. Work on Bracken compost continues.

Already it is proving economically viable in the retail trade with stockists and gardeners prepared to try it. The New Forest product was marketed at realistic but cheaper prices than either local or imported peat. Expansion of the trade would not only help conserve our wetlands from peat extraction but some of our important nature reserves from inundation by the Bracken - already a Norfolk nurseryman has been taking Bracken from the Suffolk reserve at Sandlings Heath. Sales will help fund conservation. Similarly, hill farmers could get a financial return from their Bracken instead of the immense cost of trying to control its spread through their scant pasture grasses.

If all this is raising fears that the Bracken will become a threatened plant, harvested to extinction - fear not. There will still be the sculptural croziers pushing up in the spring, the rolling swathes of golden autumn colour and the rich mahogany litter in the winter sunshine. Any harvesting will only be viable where there are extensive stands of the fern, over sites that can be readily cut, preferably by machine. There are other conservation concerns to be taken into account such as trying to safeguard the rare native Wild Gladiolus (*Gladiolus illyricus*) which grows among the fronds in the New Forest. On these sites the Bracken cannot be cut until after the Gladiolus has shed its seeds. The same applies where the alien, *Gladiolus communis, (syn G. byzantinus)* has naturalised on some Dorset and other south coast heaths and is being conserved. Timing must also take into account when the fern is least toxic, for some of the toxins are carcinogenic.

There has been much concern about possible cancer risks from inhaling the spores but this link is so far unsubstantiated It is thought, however, to be unwise to push through Bracken thickets in high summer when the fern is releasing its spores. It doesn't do this *every* year though. It has a good spore year and then rests for a couple, when it may not produce any at all. People who have to work amongst it at sporing time are advised to take precautions against inhalation. The summer air is likely to be full of spores and pollen from thousands of species of plants and fungi and so the presence of Bracken spores is inevitable and unavoidable and should not cause alarm.

Safety has been an important consideration in the development of the modern Bracken composts and tests have shown that it is safe. The dead litter does not contain carcinogens while the green material is taken either in July before spores develop or in September and October after their release and when the general levels of carcinogens in the plant are declining. Those that do remain are destroyed in the heat generated by decomposition of the compost heaps. The compost material is not made available until the following spring when degradation is complete and the product is safe.

(Inf. on current compost research by kind permission of Dr.Rona Pitman)

PIG FOOD

Bracken is the only British fern to have been eaten, by man and beast, on a large scale. Animal feed can be severely limited in the heathlands which are, by their very nature, devoid of good grassland, both for grazing and for hay. The alternatives of Ling, Gorse and Bracken were exploited instead. In the case of Bracken both the underground rhizomes and the croziers were used. References to digging out the Bracken's rhizomes are not likely to refer to heathland sites so much as to the richer soils of the arable lands, which, by their higher status, are better recorded. Such removal is perhaps best thought of as 'weeding' and was perhaps achieved by following the plough over shallow soils. On deeper soils well established Bracken would be growing too deeply to be caught by the share. Harvesting the rhizomes helped reduce a serious pest which would otherwise have to be pulled or cut by hand:- *"Let him...carve asunder with his hook the bushes and the fern, so that the corn may come heavy with ear."*

(Boethius: *De Consolatione Philosophia*)

The rhizomes were gathered primarily for feeding the pigs. Apparently they relished them, when boiled to a pulp. It is also well recorded that pigs liked to grub up rhizomes for themselves but when this was tested with modern breeds only lean ones were in the slightest bit interested! Alternatively, the croziers were picked and boiled. with much quoted instances from the Forest of Dean where girls collected and sold croziers at 2d a bushell. These were taken home for 'cooking' in the boiler-house which was adjacent to many homes as an outhouse where the laundry was boiled in the 'copper'. Therein Furze was an important fuel.

This use of the croziers as food would cause concern today as the plant is known to be toxic and some of the toxins are carcinogenic. These include the enzyme thiaminase which leads to the condition known in pigs and horses as 'the staggers' by causing a deficiency of thiamine (vitamin B_1), resulting in poor co-ordination, followed by convulsions and then death. Thiaminase also causes cancer in bone marrow and the digestive system. It is found mostly in the rhizomes and croziers. Another agent causes an acute haemorrhagic disease in sheep and cattle. It is thought to be a naturally occurring substance that mimics radiation and thereby causes mutations and cancer. This can be passed on through milk and urine.

(Inf. courtesy Ministry of Agriculture)

BREAD AND BREW

All parts of Bracken can be poisonous and should not be consumed, either as food or in home-made remedies. There are some strains of the plant that are said to be devoid of the toxins, or, of the enzymes which in turn produce the toxins, but these cannot be detected by simply looking and so *all* Bracken should be avoided. Perhaps these safer versions were once far more common which might explain why Bracken was once so widely used as cattle fodder. Bracken spreads by way of its creeping underground rhizomes which are full of starch and very nutritious. They were reportedly used for making bread flour but such reports may well be repetition of earlier statements and even those appear to be predominantly foreign (Canary Islands, France, New Zealand, North America). When it comes to seeking proof from the British Isles it is a different matter. There is a rare reference from 1480 when William Caxton reported:

> *"Poure people made their brede of fern roots."*
> (Chronicles of England)

Then in 1862 C. P. Johnson published his *Useful Plants of Great Britain* wherein he claimed personal experience:

"The writer can bear testimony to the nutritive qualities of the rhizomes of our native Brake, having frequently eaten them in considerable quantities. They should be first roasted over a fire until the outer skin is charred, and then the fibres separated by beating, the starchy substance that remains tastes much like oat cake, but with a slight astringency that is not unpleasant. Few substances will keep off hunger during violent exertion better than the underground stem of the Brake."

In the 19th century people blanched the croziers as a substitute for Asparagus. This met with particular favour in Canada and the North Eastern United States and more ideas and recipes were published in Britain during the food shortages of the First World War. Ultimately it became a major commodity in countries like Japan which started importing it to satisfy the demand for this 'appetizer'. Simultaneously Japan was developing the highest incidence of gastric cancer and a link between the two was established.

Drinks brewed with the rhizomes as an alternative to Hops are reported widely from Siberia *"and other places"* but where is the original documentation for this? Gerard said that *"the root of the Ferne cast into a hogshead of wine keepeth it from souring,"* which is as close as could be traced.

Baking, brewing and similar activities brought Bracken into use as a fuel - a usage that was important in those areas where it was easy to get. It burns readily when dried and produces a fierce heat. That made it ideal for bringing pots and kettles to the boil and the brightness of the flames must have made it popular for domestic use in dark medieval rooms and kitchens, for it was used by all the social classes, not just the poor. For heating bread ovens it was ideal, not only because of its intense heat but for the speed with which the fuel burnt out, so allowing the baker to get on with his job. Brewers used it too, or had it forced on them: in 1621 Sir Robert Boyle agreed to Mr. Green of Tallagh becoming *"the common ale and beer brewer"* and that he was *"to use ffernes and heath but not wood to brew withal."*

(Grosart, A.B. 1886. The Lismore Papers, 2; Blackburne)

HOUSE-BUILDING

Bricks, tiles, thatch, mortar, limewash, daub, can all involve the grand plant that is Bracken. The fierce heat generated by burning it led to its use for firing clay for both tiles and bricks. In the Middle Ages brick-making was a very rare craft but there is an interesting record from Farnham, Surrey (which incidentally takes its name from the Bracken ferns or 'fearns' or 'farns') where, in 1348, when the Black Death was wiping out such a large proportion of the population, no buyer could be found for the Farnham Bracken, and this evidently marked the end of the local brickmaking.

(Robo, E. 1929. 'The Black Death in the Hundred of Farnham'. *Eng. Hist. Rev.* No 44)

Although bricks were so rare in the Middle Ages clay tiles were not (remember Wat *Tyler* of the Peasants Revolt) and more references to Bracken may still lurk in records relating to tileries. These may not necessarily indicate fuel but packing material, just as in later times Bracken was used for packing slates at the quarries. Richard Neve in his *The City and Country Purchaser, and Builder's Dictionary* (1703) recorded bricks being first dried with wood fuel ready for a final firing with "Bush, Furz, Heath, Brake or Fern faggots". It took 600 fern faggots to fire a kiln of 1,000 Statute bricks (each 9 ins. x 4.5 ins. x 2.25 ins.) so the Georgian enthusiasm for brick houses must have created lucrative markets for the fern gatherers.

If the roof wasn't tiled or shingled then it was usually thatched and again Bracken was exploited. In 1351 the *Statute of Labourers* gives rates of pay for tilers and *"other coverers of fern and straw"* at 3d. (only half that for their boys), so using Bracken for roofing was well established by then. The statute also makes clear that using Bracken was not restricted to the humblest buildings, for these would not be roofed by paid craftsmen. There are later references to laying the fern as 'roofing felt' upon which to bed turves or thatch with straw, so again a lot of workmanship was involved. Obviously it was a success or else it wouldn't have been used right up to the beginning of the 20th century. Indeed, it was expected to last 15-20 years and even 30 years under favourable conditions. High winds were the most destructive as they could rip it off but that is true of other thatching materials too. Good craftsmanship in setting the thatch right from the start is the key to success but on poorer homes on a short lease there was not the incentive to do this, nor to repair areas of decay whenever necessary, all of which needs to be taken into account when reading some of the criticisms of this material.

What exactly was used is not always clear, let alone the techniques employed. Stems, fronds and rhizomes have all been recorded and their various merits debated from region to region but by 1862 Johnson was able to summarise that *"the dried leaves are employed for thatching and the stalks alone are sometimes so applied in the Highlands."* Using the whole plant was often considered an inferior usage but it was of course quicker that cutting the fronds from the stems. This time element must have been crucial as the Bracken was taken from mid-September to October which was just the time when so many other crops needed harvesting, and with it the chance for valuable casual labouring. No wonder there are so many references to neglect of the thatched roofs, especially as both pulling and thatching were very time consuming.

Each Bracken stem was pulled individually, holding it with one hand under the branching and the other down near ground level. A firm grip was essential otherwise the hands were cut to shreds by the sharp fibres as the stem ran through them when tugged. A good tug dislodged any debris which would be detrimental if built

Early brickwork: Chertsey Abbey Barn

into the roof because it would hold water and hasten decay. Six such stems made a handful which was put by to be gathered into piles of about eighteen handfuls and left to dry if necessary but dry weather was highly desired for both this task and the subsequent thatching. In this way a good worker could pull a cart load of Bracken in a day - about six and a half square yards. At that rate it would take over a fortnight to garner enough for a good sized barn. Such a cart load fetched between one and five shillings in the early 19th century, but at the lower end of that scale it was not good news since a labourer could earn more for a day's work in the harvest fields - if he could get the work.

Thatchers preferred stems that had borne fronds three to four feet high - any taller and thicker and it was not so good and the stunted stuff was too short for thatching anyway. The old roof was weeded and swept with a birch broom before new thatch was added. Then work started at the eaves, securing the points of the first bundles under turfs laid along the top of the wall and this layer was not trimmed to a smart edge until the roof was complete. Instead, the next layer was added and for this work proceeded from a plank or 'thatching beam' which lay on the roof and was hooked in place by chains from ladders at either end. It was about twenty feet long, five or six inches wide and· three or four inches thick; anything less would bend under the weight of the thatcher who sat on the roof to work with his heels lodged against the beam. A sagging beam put curves into the lines of thatch, which were set against it, and those curves would show for the whole life of the thatch.

First, the stems were bent over at the branching point, taking care not to break them. Then they were trimmed at the point/root end to get equal lengths which were then added to the roof with the points against the beam. Only six stems were added at a time, so only about seven square yards could be thatched in a day. Progress was from side to side, and then layer upon layer, with about six inches showing between the layers; it must not be more than eight inches or else the rain would get in. When the ridge was reached it was capped with long turfs. The best roofs had their layers bedded in clay but even so all Bracken thatch had to be secured and for this wooden spars were driven in at regular intervals; driven in upwards so that they would conduct wet out of the roof not into it. In some parts of the country the thatch was tied on with ropes made of Ling or Birch but no reference to this from the southern heathlands was found for this study. Today's reed thatchers tie their roof on with tarred string.

The building industry used lime, which was made by burning calcareous rock, such as chalk from the Downs. This then went into the mortar mix but even timber-framed buildings could have it incorporated into the daub for the wattle infill panels, or, thick layers of limewash were applied as a weather-proofing. This is usually associated with domestic buildings but the technique extended to military architecture, where it is thought to have given White Castle its name at Llantilio Crossenny, in Gwent. At the other extreme, labourers applied a coating of limewash to their straw hats when the autumn rains began, to extend their use through the winter before replacement the next spring. Lime was also spread on the fields to reduce the acidity. When this started is

unknown but one claimant has it recorded on his monument in the nave floor of Cranleigh parish church, Surrey. Liming was more effective than the older system of marling with calcareous clay but of course it cost a lot more, so marling continued for a few more generations.

(for lime-burning see also Furze).

THE BONFIRE WOMEN

Bracken is rich in potassium which can be extracted by burning the fern down to ashes, known as potash. The product had great commercial value, as fertilizer and as one of the basic raw materials in the manufacture of glass and soap.

Potash is potassium carbonate (K_2CO_3), used by growers to promote good roots, fruits and flowers. It appears as the 'K' reading on lists of ingredients on proprietory fertilizer packets. K comes from the Latin 'kalium' from the Arabic 'kali', used anciently for such vegetable ashes; hence 'alkaline'. They came to be called potash by the 17th century after the pots or large iron pans used in the processing. Water was passed through the ashes and caught in these pots and boiled (presumably fired with more fern to make more ashes). The potassium dissolved out of the ashes into the water and remained in the pots when boiled dry.

It is the youngest fronds that have the highest concentration of potassium but it gradually leaches out with the summer rains as the fronds unfurl and expand. Despite this the highest yields per acre are obtained in July and August, as the stems begin to yellow, due to the sheer volume of material available, making it the richest source of potash of any heathland plant. When needs demanded, other heathland plants, particularly Ling, were pressed into service and on wet heaths even the sedges and rushes. Thus from 1669 we learn that: *"those who burn Brakes for their ashes do it while they are green and strong, cutting them down and give fire to them, and so let them burn in great heaps, with a smouldering fire: whereas if they should let them turn yellow, and burn them, they would not get (as they find by experience), half so much Salt."* (W.Simpson, *Hydrologica chymica: or a cheymical anatomy of Scarborough, and other Spaws in York-shire. London 1669*)

The "great heaps", according to another description, comprised one to two cart loads. Such a heap could take several days to burn through because the ashes had to be turned regularly, until all the reddish greyness had been burnt down to white. By the 18th century, when production is considered to have been highest, this was largely women's work. This was reflected in the pricing. In 1762 the inferior ash from burnt wood cost 3d per pound whereas the much richer fern ash was merely half that. It is thought the large difference was caused by the heavy wood incurring more expensive labour charges, for the men and horses to shift the timber, whereas women and children could handle the lighter fern unaided. By 1831 Britain was importing 35,000 tons of potash from Canada (still one of the world's three greatest producers) and these imports, together with the abolition of the Salt Duty, brought home production to an end, as a major commercial enterprise.

GLORIOUS GLASS

The manufacture of glass owes much to Bracken. Items like early domestic drinking glasses have, on the whole, decayed away but despite the ravages of time and troubles glorious medieval stained glass windows still survive. The basic raw material is silica and so the earliest glass was little more than melted sand. To melt or fuse sand needs a temperature of about 1,982°C which was a great challenge in early days (glass beads date from about 2,500 BC; sculpted glass from about 2,000 BC and the first blown glass from the end of the lst century BC) until it was discovered that by adding certain other chemicals the melting point could be lowered. These 'fluxes' were primarily soda (from ashes of certain maritime plants) and potash (primarily from Bracken). The earliest references are to soda glass (1700 BC) with potash glass not being developed until the l0th century:

"By about AD 1000 a fundamental change had taken place in the glass-making of northern Europe. Presumably because of increased difficulties with communication with the Mediterranean area, the glass-makers turned from soda as a fluxing agent to potash derived from the woodlands in which they worked. The main sources were beech and bracken."
(Charleston, R.J.; English Glass and the Glass Used in England circa 400-1940. Allen and Unwin; 1984)

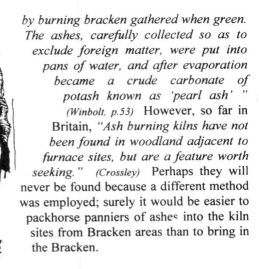

Potash glass came to dominate, although soda glass persisted in coastal locations. The new glass was harder and more translucent than soda glass but more difficult to work as the molten mass becomes rigid rather rapidly. There are various ways of getting the potash but for glass-making we read that, *"The potash required for the flux or dissolving agent was obtained*

(Illustrations: above & opposite- Byfleet, top three- Leatherhead)

by burning bracken gathered when green. The ashes, carefully collected so as to exclude foreign matter, were put into pans of water, and after evaporation became a crude carbonate of potash known as 'pearl ash' "
(Winbolt, p.53) However, so far in Britain, *"Ash burning kilns have not been found in woodland adjacent to furnace sites, but are a feature worth seeking."* (Crossley) Perhaps they will never be found because a different method was employed; surely it would be easier to packhorse panniers of ashes into the kiln sites from Bracken areas than to bring in the Bracken.

The English glass industry of the Middle Ages was centred in the Weald, totalling some twenty two known sites and probables. The prime district was astride the Surrey and Sussex border, around Chiddingfold and Kirdford. Today the parish churches at both places contain memorial windows to those early glass-makers of the district, which are composed of small quarries of glass found in later times at the furnace sites; the Chiddingfold · window has 427 pieces from the 13th-16th centuries. The general rule is that coloured glass was imported while the 'white' glass was the local product because there is a lack of evidence for the making of coloured glass at an early date in England. To complicate matters some of the imported coloured glass is thought to have gone back to the English centres to be used as cullet.

The English centre was well placed for getting fuel, being down in the vast Wealden forest, while the hills to the north (Blackdown, Hascombe, etc.) provided both Bracken and sand. They mixed two parts (by volume) with one part of silica. The local sand was not entirely ideal, for it was contaminated with iron and that gives the distinctive greenish colour to the 'white' local glass. This can be seen clearly in the windows of such churches as Ockham in Surrey.

The ashes contained other significant chemicals apart from potassium and these could be exploited too, particularly those that created colours. By the 12th/13th century it was realised that purples and flesh colours (which came from manganese) could be obtained by using ashes from Beech (*Fagus sylvatica*) and this timber was the prime fuel. It fired the furnaces as billets, *not* as charcoal as is sometimes claimed, according to G. H. Kenyon. So the glass-makers were saving their own ashes as another source of potash (which is perhaps why archaeologists cannot find potash kilns at the glass-making sites). Beech provided the best fuel because it burns so readily and hotly. It burns very fast too and so large amounts must have been needed, yet the tree was far from being as common then, in that district, as it is today. It is not surprising then that Kenyon has identified Oak and Birch billets as other favoured fuels. Even so coloured glass continued to be imported (primarily from Normandy and the Rhineland). Potash glass is often known as 'fougère glass' which is simply the French name for Bracken. In the reign of Elizabeth I foreign workers, often described as Huguenot refugees, arrived with Continental techniques which included the rejection of potash, so that

"the only reasonably safe assumption seems to be that the fine quality glass was first made in the Weald in 1567 by Jean Carré using barilla soda instead of the wood or bracken ash."

(Kenyon, G.H. Some Notes on Wealden Glass; Notes and Reviews of the Society of Glass Technology. Vol.35. 1951. p.11)

Carré is reputedly buried at Alfold, Surrey, under the slab of Sussex marble in the churchyard. The church guidebook says he *"died May 27th 1572 and who was one of the last of the French glassmakers, whose centre of works was in the depths of Sidney wood in the parish. Jean Carré was responsible for introducing into this country glassmakers from Lorraine and obtained a licence in 1567 to manufacture 'glass for glazing such as is made in France, Burgundy, and Lorraine.' "*

Another impurity was calcium which it was realised, in 1689, improved the toughness of the glass. However, by then the industry had left the Weald. This move was due to the introduction of coal as a furnace fuel (c.1611) and had nothing to do with what Kenyon called that "strangely persistent myth" that the Wealden woodlands were exhausted.

With thanks for assistance from the librarian of the Surrey Archaeological Society, and with special reference to:-

Charleston, R.J.; (1984) *English Glass and the Glass Used in England circa 400-1940.* Allen and Unwin;
Crossley, David; (1993)*; Monuments Protection Programme - The Glass Industry.* Step 1; Report. English Heritage.
Kenyon, G.H., Some Notes on Wealden Glass; *Notes and Reviews of Soc. of Glass Technology*; Vol.35; 1951
- (1956-7); Some Notes on the Glass Industry in England Prior to 1567; *Journal of the Brit. Soc. of Master Glass-Painters*; Vol XXII; No.2)
- (1967); *The Glass Industry of the Weald*; Leicester Univ. Press.
Winbolt, S.E., (1932); Wealden Glass: The Old Surrey and Sussex Glass Industry; *Trans. Soc. of Glass Technology* ;Vol.16;
- (1933); *Wealden Glass : The Surrey-Sussex Glass Industry*; Combridges, Hove.

POTASH FOR LYE AND SOAP MAKING

When water was run through the Bracken ashes for making potash it produced an alkaline solution known as 'lye'. This was found to combine with grease and oil and so be an effective cleaner, or, it could be combined with animal fat to make a ball of soap. The Greeks and Romans knew this but appeared to have used it only in health care, until the 2nd century AD, while in England it was not until the 10th century that the Saxons started to exploit its full potential. These alkaline cleaners could also have a bleaching action and together were invaluable for cleaning the oily sheep fleeces for the developing wool trade. Ultimately England's wealth depended upon this wool and cloth industry.

Making lye became the responsibility of women. The work involved placing sticks in the bottom of a perforated container which was then lined with a cloth. Potash was heaped in and then water. The solute ran through the cloth which was kept from clogging the perforations by the sticks and so it was able to drip through into a second container positioned beneath. This lower container was called the 'buck', from the languages of Saxon times. Buck also came to mean both the lye itself and the wool or cloth being treated with the lye; hence the term 'buck-wash' and the process was 'bucking'.

At its simplest, the solute dripping into the buck was ready for use, simply because it had potassium dissolved into it but it might be too weak to be very effective. That was overcome by evaporating off excess water to increase the chemical concentration, either by slow natural exposure to the air or by boiling. Fuel for the fire provided more ashes.

By the l5th century it was being boiled with tallow and thickened with bean flour so that the paste could be moulded by hand into balls. These were dried out by the fire as 'soap' and would last for years if somehow kept dry in the damp homes. In households with servants, up to the 17th century, soap was bought as an import from Venice and Spain and then the still-room maids converted it into balls after adding gums, oils and scent. At that time rosewater was very fashionable and could have the scent of violets added by the use of orris root. There were spiced versions too, with such familar ingredients as cloves, nutmeg and cinnamon. As for the size of the balls, they were described by Parkinson in l640 as *"good big balls"* but as he says *"foure of these balls being dissolved in warme water is sufficient to wash a whole bucke full of clothes,"* they do not sound much larger than would fit comfortably in the palm of the hand for scrubbing.

For soap-making the basic mixture was one pint of lye to two pounds of mutton fat, which was then simmered for several hours. Then the glutinous mixture was ready to pour into wooden moulds lined with cloths and left to set. Finally the cloths could be pulled off and the soap cut into blocks ready for use. Any household could make their own quite easily but only if they could spare the time from their other work and so the specialist soap-maker came into being. For many the actual making of the soap could well have been a seasonal occupation when the ashes were available, stockpiling the product for sale throughout the year. Others could have stocked up with ashes. Soap-makers are not always easy to trace in old records, despite the importance of their trade. This suggests much of the work was seasonal and is disguised in the records under the name of another occupation - perhaps chandling (candle-making) since that also used mutton fat.

The summer burnings for Bracken ash became an important seasonal occupation for women right across the country to Ireland. Thus there was a glut of soap balls at the start of the season when they could be bought for 3d. a dozen (in the l840s) but as winter dragged on and the stocks dwindled so the prices increased up to 8d. a dozen. Many were destined for the houses in local towns but the market was so good that it was worthwhile (according to Celia Fiennes in l695) transporting them all the way to London from Staffordshire, they being, as she says, *"easily sent about."*

The soap balls destined for personal cleanliness came to be coloured and scented. There was a particularly wide range of vegetable dyes available since the colourant did not have to be permanent. It is said that households utilised the coloured water from cooking 'greens', carrots or beetroots. This could only have been possible in later times when such vegetables became available and when they were cooked separately. Scent was taken from such herbs

as Rosemary and Lavender which have oils that are not only aromatic but also antiseptic. Rosemary was not introduced (or re-introduced) into this country until 1348 but Lavender came with the Romans - the name Lavender comes from the Roman word 'lavare' meaning to wash.

Commercial production of soaps seems to have ended the Bracken-based product, by the l860s. It is still commemorated in a few place names, because the use of lye caused that word to transfer to the washing green itself. Thus next to Woking, Surrey, is the open space known as St. John's Lye, still remembered as being covered with clothes lines in 1928. It's beside the Basingstoke Canal and the name lye for a washing green seems to have persisted particularly well in relation to bargees and inland waterways.

'The Old Soap House' West Horsley 1962; information and illustration courtesy of local historian, Pam Bowley.

Local names may help trace centres of soap-making. Thus one old house at West Horsley, Surrey, was known unofficially as 'The Old Soap House' and during refurbishment in the 1960s one of the rooms downstairs was found to have its walls impregnated with a chemical that must have been stacked against it. This was thought to have been potassium carbonate. Interestingly, the garden was the only one in the village with Soapwort (*Saponaria officinalis*). This beautiful scented plant got its name from its use, for the saponin content of the sap creates a lather - hence Latherwort and Fullers' Herb. Anyone who has tried to eradicate this plant from their garden will readily believe that those tenacious creeping rhizomes could have persisted from the 1630s! When this plant came into use is unknown and even its status as a native is far from certain.

CHAMOIS

Bracken gets mentioned regularly in the context of tanning but by a succession of authors repeating each other. Additional material seems to be missing entirely. Apparently astringent properties in the rhizomes were extracted by decoction for the dressing and preparation of kid and chamois leather. The source of this information is never quoted but the earliest reference is thought to be Lightfoot's *Flora Scotica* of 1777 but even that is thought to derive from earlier reports, probably from countries other than Britain.

MOSQUITOES

Burning Bracken to ward off insects such as gnats and mosquitoes was in print by 1579 with Langham's *Garden of Health* and was repeated in 1640 by Parkinson who reported that,

"fume of ferne being burned driveth away Serpents, Gnats, and other Noisome creatures that in the Fenny Countries much molest both strangers and inhabitants that lye in bed at night time, with their faces uncovered."

This was repeated almost verbatim by Culpeper in 1658. Gardeners have long known that an insecticide for aphids can be made from water in which green Bracken has been boiled while modern research in India (reported in Britain 1993) found that extracts from Bracken were indeed insecticidal, not only against aphids but also the destructive diamond-back moth.

MEDICINAL

Many an ailment was treated with Bracken yet it failed to achieve the lasting esteem held by many other herbs. To the herbalists this plant was the 'Female Fern' which should not be confused with the Lady Fern, *Athyrium felix-femina*, even though the Latin name used by the herbalists was *Felix femina*. In Langham's *The Garden of Health* of 1579 there are 21 recipes to which others have been added since, for the treatment of broken skin, burns, the canker, constipation, cot deaths, mosquito bites, horsesickness, hypochondria, internal obstructions, nosebleeds, painful sinews, rickets, sciatica, sores, spleen problems, ulcers, worms, and wounds including galling by cattle and festering wounds. It was also called upon for purgation. Of these the worm treatment appears to have been the most important use, but not for women - Bracken was known to *"maketh women barren"* and Turner (1562) warns, *"They are not good to be given unto women who have many children; neither are they good to go much over for women who are already with child."* He recommends its use as a vulnerary for burns, scalds and ulcers that are stubborn to heal. Today, Bracken is not listed in the British Pharmacopoeia although herbal medicine books are still being published containing recipes with Bracken but this toxic plant should be left strictly for professional use

CARNATIONS

Carnation growers were instructed by Gertrude Jekyll in her *Wood and Garden* (1899), how to make pegs for pinning down layers for rooting. After alerting the reader to choose stout stems she then reports:

"The cut fern is lightly laid in a long ridge with the ends all one way, and the operator sits at the stalk end of the chosen ridge. Four cuts with the knife make a peg, and each frond makes three pegs in about fifteen seconds. In about four days the pegs dry to a surprising hardness; they are better than wooden ones, and easier and quicker to make."

SPHAGNUM MOSS

Sphagnum spp.

The particular beauty of the Sphagnum moss is unrivalled on the wet heathlands. Their hummocks and cushions and undulating blankets give a soft rounded form just where it would otherwise be lacking. The colours, from sharpest green to grey-green, to bronze and red, surprise the blackened soil around and reflect doubly in the black bog water. In droughts they dry almost white, look dead, feel papery and disappointing until wetted once more. Then, as if by some weird magic, they swell back, green up and grow once more. Whorl upon whorl of branches grow out of the stems in their own peculiar way, unique to the Sphagnums. To see them rimed with silver frost is to see one of the great beauties of the heathlands.

As the ice sheets receded at the end of the last Ice Age then the thawed surface of Britain became a tundra landscape of lichens and mosses. Chief of these mosses, were the species of Sphagnum, so resistant to cold and desiccating winds, so enthusiastic about wet conditions. Thus they are sometimes called Bog Mosses and a north country bog is called a 'moss'. Botanically they are known collectively as Sphagnales and there are about thirty species and many varieties in Britain today.

These plants continued to flourish when the climate warmed and began supporting the wider range of plants that attracted herds of grazing animals that in turn attracted man, as a hunter. We learn from archaeological finds that Stone Age man put these mosses to wise and good uses that are still valid today. Therefore Sphagnum mosses must have served man in Britain for longer than any other green plant (lichens excepted; maybe clubmosses run parallel).

They have been exploited for their healing qualities and for their softness cum absorbancy. The unique branching system of whorls meshes together to make a wonderful warm padding, with the softness being retained as the plant dries out - just what those prehistoric peoples needed in the icy climate and so it was they who invented thermal underwear! It has also been used to line anoraks and other over-garments; to wrap babies, line their cradles and pad their carrying boards (cradle boards, papoose boards). Adults have slept on it, just have pigs but references to this (recorded as gathering 'moth' in Surrey) refer to an infrequent use. Even lead roofs and other fittings were bedded on it, to prevent damage during the expansion and contraction of the metal through the changing temperatures. Thus we read in the building accounts (1602-7) of Ashley House, Walton-upon-Thames (courtesy of the Surrey Record Office) entries such as paying *"more for mosse for the conditt head and vautes ramminge."*

It has the capacity to absorb sixteen times its own weight of water, which is twice as much as cotton wool. As it dries out it does not lose its ability to absorb moisture back into the cells; indeed it will come back to life and herbarium specimens have done just that after decades. One exploitation of this characteristic has been as a baby's nappy liner - a practice that developed into making a special pouch for moss in the nappy (and later in the pants). A strip was cut from the side of the nappy cloth and sewn back in the centre, leaving one narrow end open, to make the pouch for stuffing with moss, and this was strategically positioned when the nappy was applied. This hardly hindered the baby's first steps at all, compared with all the baggage slung between the baby's legs today. These moss pouches were still being used in Surrey in 1953/4   (see *'Daisy Chains* -in this series)

Another exploitation of its absorbancy has been for wound dressings - to mop up free blood and to draw out puss and poisons. Recent archaeological finds have taken this usage back to the Stone Age. Florence Nightingale is said to have had ship loads of it sent out to her during the Crimean War. It was in use again during both the First and Second World Wars. The latest official use traced for this study is 1969 at Maidenhead, Berks. It was safe to use as it is sterile from having grown in acidic conditions. Indeed it is now known to be anti-microbial and to promote healing but what exactly the moss contains for achieving this has eluded modern science.

The 20th century also saw vast amounts being taken both for the making of wreaths, where it was employed to stuff the core inside the wire frame, and for horticultural use, where it served as a water-retaining liner for hanging baskets. At the end of the season when the baskets had finished, gardeners were advised to save it, chop it small and mix into the potting compost. Today there are alternative materials available and wherever possible the use of Sphagnales should be avoided. They are slow growing and under threat from over collection, even on sites where they are supposed to be protected by law. To many people it is 'just moss' and they give it scant respect and yet this plant contains those mysterious healing properties which are still not understood fully but which may one day save thousands of lives.

Church Jump.
Devil's Punch Bowl
7.7.1978.

DEVIL'S PUNCH BOWL, 1911:-

"But the boggy character is most apparent in the upper end of the great valley - that part nearest to the Gibbet Hill ridge. Here, not only the bottom, but the sloping sides, form one morass. Everywhere is the light green of Sphagnum moss, with its tufted cushiony growth, wettest and softest in the middle where it rises highest. The water squeezes out of it as from a sponge. Growing frequently with it, also in tufts, but the tufts keeping a level surface instead of the swelling form of the bog-moss, and less spongy in its texture is the dark green of the hair moss [Polytrichum commune]. Both of these mosses lose all of their form and beauty when taken from the water wherein they live, and dried. The light green, feathery bog-moss becomes faded and whitish green - a shrunken, limp and uninteresting plant; whilst the hair moss instantly folds its delicate, filamentous leaves upwards, and its star-like growth becomes merely so many dark green stalks. The bog plants require the setting of the bog."

(Matthews, E.C., 1911, *The Highlands of South West Surrey*, Black)

Only small patches of Sphagnum survive in The Devil's Punch Bowl today. Trees have overgrown much of the site described above, although the National Trust is working to reclaim the surviving heathland.

GORSE or FURZE or WHIN

Ulex europaeus L.
Ulex gallii Planchon
Ulex minor L.

Gorse, Whin or Furze are the three commonest names for one of the most distinctive heathland shrubs; the only one that is covered with very sharp spines so that anyone who doesn't know a Daisy from a Dock will know when they have found this! To a botanist Furze is not one species but three. By far the commonest, and most robust, is the Common or European Gorse, *Ulex europaeus*, which is the prime species of the old records outlined in this section. It likes the maritime climate of the British Isles and so it doesn't do nearly so well on the Continent. Thus conserving our Furze and its associated wildlife is important when the European lowland heaths are reviewed as a whole. A second species, which is dwarfer and flowers at a different time, with a different shade of yellow, is *Ulex gallii*, the Western Gorse. This has the greatest preference for a maritime climate and is therefore most often found around western heaths within the influences of the Atlantic. There are a few exceptions such as a coastal site in Suffolk. Thirdly there is *Ulex minor*, known as Dwarf Gorse or Lesser Gorse which is the least robust and therefore unsuited to some of the uses here described but it's just as savage round the walker's ankles.

Gorse, Furze and Whin are all ancient names brought by early colonisers. It was possibly the Scandinavians (Vikings etc.) who brought the word 'whin' for it has persisted particularly well in regions which they colonised, such as parts of Ireland, (in some places Whin is used regularly in the plural as Whins). The Germanic peoples (Angles, Saxons, etc.) brought the names 'gorse' and 'furze'. Oldest is possibly gorse, which is thought to derive from the Indoeuropean word 'ghrzd' which meant rough or prickly and gave rise to other names for rough plants, such as the Latin 'hordeum' for Barley. Furze was also descriptive, coming from old words

for plants with evergreen needles, hence 'firs' for conifers. These are the names of long standing which have changed little through the centuries, being short, easy to remember and easy to use. There are a few newer British names such as Fingers-and-thumbs or Thumbs-and-Fingers, French Furze, Honey-bottle, Pins-and-needles. It's even been called Ling like the *Calluna* heather. Country people know it widely and simply as *Fuzz* or *Goss*. In many counties it is invariably Furze or Fuzz until c.1900 and then usage changes suddenly to Gorse.

These plants were found to be extremely useful, especially as they will grow under conditions most plants find unfavourable. With this long association with man it is not surprising that they are rich in ancient folklore, much of it now shared with the Broom, and suggesting an association with pagan fertility rites. The widely held belief that the Common Furze is in flower throughout the year is not true: sad for lovers since, *When Gorse is out of bloom, so kissing is out of season* and also for debtors who claim, *I'll pay my bills when Gorse is out of flower.* Such lore must have originated on the western heaths where a mixture of all three species would provide a greater continuity of bloom. Country lore also decrees that bringing these flowers indoors, particularly during May, is taboo. Whether this, or possibly other lore now lost, has affected the annual cycle of usage has not been ascertained for this study.

In earliest times man must have discovered that the twiggy growth, when dead and dry, is highly inflammable and blazes both brightly and hotly. As the early peoples began to establish permanent sites and turn to agriculture so the Furze proved valuable in many ways, which led to the growing, harvesting and selling of Furze becoming a specific occupation, for people known variously as a furzer, furze cutter, faggot cutter, faggoter, or something recognisably similar. Like any other occupation it developed its own techniques, tools, language, practices, and rituals which varied from district to district around the British Isles and so the following is a particularly generalised summary.

SOURCES OF FURZE

Furze was so valuable it was treated with respect and managed as a renewable resource. The idea that it could be taken from the manorial 'waste' should be treated with caution as in some places it was too valuable; for example a description of the Manor of Eastbury, at Compton, Surrey, in 1572 includes 40 acres of Furze and heath separately from the 'waste', indicating its value. (Boston)

Alternatively, some could be taken as a partial harvest from bushes serving other purposes, such as using the clippings from the Furze hedges in Cornwall. The best solution was to grow it deliberately, for cropping. This could be as a field crop as we would think of it today, or, as a type of 'set-aside' to utilise part of a field being used for other purposes, even as pasture. This was known as a 'furze break'. It was also grown as widely spaced rows across open land to leave room for pasture or other crops between.

Thickets could be created to double up as protection for game, bee hives, lambing folds etc. Furze was very versatile and our ancestors adept at exploiting it.

GROWING FIELDS OF FURZE FROM SEED

Field crops are not to be expected in a book on heathlands but fields of Furze were sown deliberately and these created a heath all of their own, even if only a temporary one. When such fields were allowed to grow on towards maturity they must have created a wonderful habitat for birds such as the Stonechat, Dartford Warbler (known in some districts as a Furze Wren) and Whinchat (named after the shrub).

The need for seed was satisfied either by the farmer or his family collecting their own from the hard black seed pods or by buying it. The idea of buying seeds sounds familiar enough today but at some unknown date in history Furze seed must have come on to the market for the first time, signifying not simply a demand but one great enough to finance the collection of the seed and its retailing. By the 17th century it was an important crop for returning land to fertility as Furze is a leguminous plant - capable of putting nitrogen into the soil - and by then the seed merchants, as we think of them, had come into being. Nevertheless, there must have been people, presumably women and children, who were paid a few pennies for hours and hours spent on the finger stabbing job of collecting the seed pods. How the seeds were released seems to have gone unrecorded. Possibly the pods were pounded in a linen bag or, more likely, the bag was left in the sun to make the ripe pods explode in the usual way - these are the people, tasks and techniques that have escaped documentation, leaving us to deduce their former existence. The extent of local trade, if any, is unknown, but Furze seed could be bought from seedsmen in the big centres, such as from William Lucas at his shop with the sign of The Naked Boy or The Three Naked Boys, in the Strand, London, in 1677. (see John Harvey)

Plenty of seed was needed, especially if the crop was intended for animal fodder, because it was sown so thickly that *"the plant does not branch, it throws up straight, long, succulent shoots from the roots, with few or no spines along the stem, presenting no difficulty to the scythe in mowing it down. Seed should be sown in May, at the latest, and at the rate of 40 lbs to the statute and 65 lbs to the Irish acre."(The Irish Farmers' Gazette; Vol 26; 1867; Dublin)*

There are records of double cropping - sowing Furze seed with barley or oats so that after the cereal had been harvested the Furze could grow on to mature as a second crop, while at the same time replenishing the soil with nitrogen. The spines should have been absent or soft at the time of the cereal harvest otherwise this system would have been very unpopular with the reapers, and with the mowers when Furze was sown with hay seeds. Less seed per acre would have been needed under this system.

SOWING FURZE IN ROPES

An alternative to broadcast sowing was to sow in rows, either to create a hedge or a hedge-like crop in open ground. Instead of sowing in drills there was the rope method of great antiquity. It was described by the ancient Greek writer, Democritus, and that was copied in 1577 by Thomas Hill for *The Gardener's Labyrinth* (the first popular gardening book in English) wherein he instructs upon the collection of fruits and seeds for making a mixed hedge and decrees, *"mix and steep for a time, all the Berries and seeds in the binding meale of Tares, unto the thickness of honey: the same mixture lay diligently into old and untwisted Ship or Wel-ropes, or other long worne ropes, and fittered or broken into short pieces, being in the manner starke rotten, in such order, that the seeds bestowed or couched within the soft haires of them, may be preserved and defended from the cold, unto the beginning of spring."* Then, he explains, the rope should be unrolled into a drill along the route of the proposed hedge, covered lightly with soil and watered if necessary. This same principle, but adjusted specifically for Furze, was recorded from Ireland by A.T. Lucas. The main difference was that in Ireland the rope was made specifically for Furze, from hay or straw, and soaked in horse manure to give it nutrients to foster the seedlings; the rope itself would have added organic matter and retained moisture. The practice was developed sufficiently for such ropes to acquire their own name, 'súgán', and to be twisted by a special tool, also with its own name, 'crúicin'. The seeds were inserted 18ins apart and the rope rolled out into a channel etc. in the ancient Greek method. It's difficult to imagine that all this was worth the effort but evidently it was. Inevitably there were those who simply ploughed or dug a channel and sowed the seeds direct, brushing in bonfire ashes as a potash fertilizer (using a Furze branch as the

brush of course) and then harrowing the soil over the top with a Furze branch.

HARVESTING FURZE

Young Furze yields to scythe and sickle while older Furze requires some form of billhook. The best type of sickle was a traditional one with the serrated edge, while the best scythe was the modified 'furze scythe' which had its back strengthened at the time of forging (rather than having a strip rivetted on afterwards) and it had a shorter blade than did a grass scythe. The sickles were in use long before scythes were invented.

The hooked stick that was normally used with a sickle was changed for a T-shaped stick when used with Furze. It needed to be at least a foot long and was sometimes two and a half times that, with prongs up to six inches long, used for pinning down the stems against the draw of the blade. Then it served to rake up cut stems and to fork them up, while protecting the worker's hands. This is for young Furze, cut in its second or third year and probably less than eighteen inches high. The growth rate varied with the growing conditions around the British Isles and so harvesting had to be adjusted to suit the intended purpose of the crop. Rev. H. Townsend was expecting it to be left until the third year when he wrote: *"It may well be very well worth the farmer's pains to devote an acre or two to furze: after the third year's growth from seed it will afford an abundant annual cutting."* (Munster Farmers' Mag.; Cork; Vol.1; 1812; p.36)

Young Furze intended for animal fodder was best cut while still succulent and soft. Once the tissue had started to harden extra work would be needed for crushing the spines prior to feeding. Otherwise, hardening stems that would still yield to scythe and sickle were ideal for fuel. Woody stems needed attacking with a billhook but the spiny shrub was by this stage well able to attack back and so billhooks were sometimes provided with leather wrist guards. The left hand was protected by a leather glove or more usually a mitten, although some Irish had a technique of binding the hand with rope. Leather leggings were worn too, usually coming up over the knee, but sometimes on the left leg only.

The cut stems were bundled and taken home for binding up into the faggots. That way no useful trimmings were left to waste out in the countryside. Lucas published a description of the art of bundling:-

"A length of twine was stretched on the ground, one end being tied to a small stick stuck in the ground. The other end was tied in a groove near the lower end of a much' longer stick, called a 'bock', which was also stuck upright in the ground, so that the twine was held at full stretch. The furze sticks were then laid traversely across the string and packed up against the 'bock'. When enough had been heaped up to make a bundle of the proper size, the 'bock' was pulled up, bringing the end of the twine with it which was taken round the bundle and tied to the end attached to the small stick." (p.49)

Where twine was not available they used 'withes' made from willow, a long shoot of Furze itself or barked bramble shoots. The last were sometimes called 'briars' but should not be confused with roses or heather. Thomas Hardy's 'Clym Yeobright' went *"in search of brambles for faggot-bonds."* He was also described as *"busily chopping away at the furze, a long row of faggots which stretched downward from his position representing the labour of the day."* (*Return of the Native*)

MAKING FAGGOTS

Whether made in the countryside or at home the bundles of Furze stems destined to be sold had to be made up into 'faggots' of standard size and quality. So important was this product that towns and cities passed laws and regulations to govern and control size, quality and price. Bearing in mind that being a faggotter could be a full-time occupation then these regulations had a major impact upon local rural life, and upon individual families if penalties were incurred.

Obviously it was crucial that the faggots be well tied to withstand the journey to town and the tossing about as they were stacked. There was such an art to this that it became an additional skill to show off at ploughing matches. The Furze, still with its heads of twiggy tops, was stacked in two bundles so that the heads were at either end and the main stems crossed in the centre. These were then tied with a figure of eight bond made from a long young shoot of Furze itself. There was a particularly clever knack of fixing one end into the other end so as to make the tie totally secure and capable of withstanding all the manhandling. Two year old Furze was highly prized for faggots so, if close-grown, the stems would not have made a particularly bushy head, nor would the stems have been so long as to pose problems. All the same, when carried on the back through narrow streets they no doubt ensured that other pedestrians gave passing space!

A good faggoter could cut and tie a hundred faggots a day and for a long time in recent history that day's work would have earned him 2/6d, whether in Ireland or Dorset. That was about one fifth of the top retail price of the hundred.

TOWN MARKETS

Today, when fuel comes instantly with the click of a switch, it is difficult to imagine the hundreds of faggots that would be needed every day by one of the large towns or cities. They were needed as fuel for both domestic hearths and industrial processing such as baking, brewing and dyeing.

Experience soon taught our ancestors that large stacks of Furze were a serious fire risk. Not only would they have been highly inflammable but would have given off such an intense heat that no one could have got close with pails of water. Consequently, in the days when towns protected themselves with walls, the regulations of the town councils forbade Furze stacks within those walls. Needless to say, bakers and brewers etc. needed a ready supply to hand and therefore flouted the regulations. Where preserved, it

is the legal proceedings against them that give an insight into this aspect of former urban life.

The business centre for faggots must therefore have been outside the walls, presumably placed convenient to a gateway. Here we have to imagine all the bustle as deliveries, in carts and back-packs, came to the borough; all the counting and checking of quality control before payment could be made. At least prices were fixed so there should not have been a lot of arguing - unless a faggot was undersized! We know from records that the officers measured them with metal hoops of the agreed standard size but trying to pass a faggot through one of these could be difficult and waste a lot of time. This led Lucas to suggest the hoop might have been split and hinged like a giant pair of calipers. In which case we can guess that the faggoters did their own measurements, perhaps by wrapping a knotted cord round the bundle, before they left for town.

We can imagine also, streams of townsfolk in the early morning light pouring through the gateway to get their daily fuel before work could begin. Fresh deliveries gave rise to new stacks and what great stacks they must have been too, since they rose higher than the city walls, causing alarm that enemies could use them to get over the walls, not to mention cheats trying to avoid paying tolls at the gateways. The height of stacks was soon regulated! Stacking was the work of two men: the 'pikeman' on the ground who pitched up the faggots with a dung fork and the 'stacker' on top who built up and shaped the stack with a hay fork. While all this was going on other stacks were being dismantled to meet the day's demand. What a wonderful habitat they must have made for rats! To aid your imaginings go to Chester where you can still travel the highway out to the former stack yard. You'll know which road because it's still called 'Gorse Stacks'.

More difficult to imagine are the busy waterfronts of towns on big rivers. No doubt many wharfingers were familiar with Furze being brought in by boat but Lucas was prompted by his researches to wonder whether in some cases the faggots were roped together and floated down as rafts. The need for these to dry out would help explain the great stacks which otherwise imply that supply exceeded demand. Otherwise the apparent surplus would be due to seasonal fluctuations. Young (two year old) growth was often cut in the spring/summer and left to dry for a few weeks before being faggotted and taken to town while mature Furze was often harvested in winter when both work and fuel were much needed.

FURZE AS FUEL

In effect two different fuels can be obtained from Furze: the twiggy tops ignite readily and burn rapidly with a fierce heat, which was ideal for bread ovens, while the thick stems burn hotly but slowly, which was ideal wherever more sustained heat was needed, as in firing bricks and tiles.

Turning to bakers first, their main problem was that their daily cycle of work could take sixteen hours and so it was crucial to have a fuel capable of producing as much heat as fast as possible. The fuel was fired in the bottom of the oven itself (until c.1835 onwards) thereby leaving a heap of ashes where the dough needed to be placed. Sweeping it out lost valuable heat while the oven door was open, but, Furze burns down to very little ash. Furthermore, the ash was not prone to have lumps of charcoal left in it, to stick in the bread crust and customers' gums. One way of getting rid of charcoal bits and loosened bits of oven brick was to get them stuck into a 'sausage' of dough rolled along the oven floor. It has been suggested this dough roll was known as 'cake' which puts a whole new complexion upon Marie Antoinette's famous remark that the Parisians starving for want of bread should eat cake. Something clogged with debris is still described as 'caked-up'.

The demand for fuel from bakers would not have been as great as might be imagined. It was not every community that had a *public* bakehouse. It was considered the hallmark of a good housewife to be able to bake her own bread and good bread at that. Only where craftsmen and their families were employed so fully that they had no time for baking did they buy bread. There was prejudice against shop bread, so that even today in Lancashire it is remembered that anyone talking rubbish was 'talking off his shop loaf'. The earliest Irish reference that Lucas could trace was of 1568. The demand for fuel for ovens is difficult to appreciate today, not knowing the size of the oven, but accounts regularly quote 2-7 faggots per firing. When accounts increase up to 30 it must surely be a public bakehouse, especially as that much fuel could cost three shillings or more. Large ovens were hot enough when the bricks began to whiten with the heat, otherwise flour was thrown on to the oven floor and if it blackened it was hot enough but if it burst into flames it was too hot. No wonder baking was such an art!

For generations the furze-cutters could sell the tops to the bakers and the older stems to the building industries and thereby balance supply and demand but by the 19th century the expanding population had made things difficult. The builders could afford higher prices and so the bakers lost out. The answer was to grow Furze as a crop specially for the bakers. Thus in 1862 Johnson reported,

"In Surrey, and other counties around the metropolis, large quantities are consumed by the bakers for heating ovens. On some of the sandy districts of western Surrey it is sown for this purpose,

being ready to cut about three years after sowing, and yielding a crop of faggots at similar intervals for several years."

This is borne out by property sales particulars in the area, such as for Potters Park Farm (Chobham and Chertsey parishes) in 1817 which listed:-

Copse and Furze Field of 4 acres 2 rods 29 perches
New Furze Field of 8 acres 9 perches
Lower Furze Field of 16 acres 3 rods 26 perches.
(Chertsey Museum; 'Chertseyana',Vol.I, 79)

Another document in the same archive relates to Halwick Manor Farm between Chertsey and Byfleet when sold in 1817:-

Furze field - 4 acres 3 rods 32 perches
Plus furze - 1 acre 3 rods 23 perches

A mile away is Ottershaw Park and the mortgage agreement for that, in 1722, lists *"160 acres of furze and heath, now unfenced,"* (Stratton) which highlights the way larger estates could fuel their own needs. Owners imposed strict regulations on the workers with regard to what surplus they were allowed for themselves and these were rarely generous - the whole idea was to keep the workers dependent and subservient.

Having fields of Furze was obviously a sound investment and 'Furze Field' occurs widely on local maps around the British Isles, plus variants such as 'Gossners' at Laleham, Middlesex. There's Furzen Farm at Alfold, Surrey, and less obvious from the same village, Figbush Farm which in 1558 was spelt Fykbush, meaning pointed, as in thorns, and could well refer to Furze. Not far off at Cranleigh is Freeswell which used to be spelt Furzehill and before that, in 1294, was Furshull. (*Surrey Place Names*)

Not all cooking was done in the oven. The famous Irish griddle bread was 'toasted' in front of the fire and there are variants upon that idea from Scotland, Wales, etc. Furze as a domestic fuel was especially valuable for the speedy rekindling of the hearth in the mornings or when returning from the fields, and to bring pots and kettles to the boil. In these cases it was known as a 'hurrier'.

Turning now to the lime-burners; these made an important demand for Furze fuel, even if only for a couple of centuries. It had long been known that fertility could be increased by marling - spreading calcareous clay of the fields. Then it was found more effective to burn calcareous rock (chalk and limestones) to make lime and to spread that on the fields. The acidic soils of the south are often within carting distance of the chalk downs, with market towns in the river gaps, so there developed the practice of bringing back chalk blocks in the empty carts after going to market, as recorded by Gertrude Jekyll:-

"Farms throughout the district [Godalming, Surrey] *had their own kilns for burning the lime. Many of these kilns have been destroyed, but a fair number remain. They were built in steeply sloping ground by or near a roadside, where the loads of chalk could be drawn up to their top level. The larger blocks of chalk were built up inside the kiln (which is circular in plan and open at the top), in the form of a rough arch, corresponding more or less to the opening, and the smaller pieces of chalk were filled in above. The space underneath was filled with furze faggots, and a certain amount of burning converted the chalk to lime."*

(1904, Old West Surrey; p.208)

(Illustration of the old lime kiln outside Hambledon Church, known to Gertrude Jekyll as she took photographs here.)

Derelict lime kiln
Hambledon, Surrey.
1990

Although she says these were circular in plan that applies usually to the interior only; the outside was regularly square. As for being open at the top, that was only until the kiln was filled with its layers of chalk or lime and fuel, after which it was sealed over with a dome of soil, leaving a central chimney type air vent. After firing and cooling the remaining mixture of soil from the dome, fuel ashes, and lime, was raked out through the basal apertures. This was 'quicklime' (calcium oxide) which is dangerously caustic until it has been doused with water to convert it to 'slaked lime' (calcium hydroxide). If it was not needed at once it could be stacked in the open to convert naturally in the rainfall. Obviously these kilns could consume vast amounts of Furze, especially in those years of the 19th century when corn harvests were poor, prices soared, people starved and there was every incentive to increase the productivity of the land. (See also fuel section for Bracken)

END OF THE FUEL TRADITION

Back in the 17th century John Evelyn had written that nothing was "more excellent" than Furze fuel and so it remained in use until the end of the 19th century for the poorer peoples of the heathlands. By then however the bustling stack yards outside the city walls had been long forgotten. Coal had taken over, both for domestic and industrial uses, and was widely available, courtesy of the Victorians' enthusiasm for railways. In the mean time the open countryside had been 'Inclosed' and many rural communities lost their

common land and their commoners' rites. The right to take fuel was usually included as part of people's 'right of estovers'. That comes from the Latin *est opus*, meaning, *it is necessary* and fuel was certainly necessary. Consequently many rural employers had to start providing fuel for their workers, as part of their wages. The canal owners developed this at an early date for their lock keepers, to reduce the risk of them leaving their posts to go 'shopping' or to steal a scoop of coal off the back of a barge. Similarly the owners of country estates made such provision for their head gardeners, gamekeepers etc. The alternative was for a provision of land to be made for the benefit of the poor. Thus at Sunbury-on-Thames the Inclosures created a new *'Fuel Land Estate'* charity: *"for the benefit of the poor of the parish of Sunbury in lieu of and in full compensation and satisfaction for all and every right or rights which was or were or might be or have been claimed by the poor of the same parish of cutting furze, heath and turf on the waste lands and grounds for fuel."*

From the same Middlesex parish it was proposed in the following year, 1801, that the inmates of the workhouse should be employed cutting furze. They were supposed to be usefully employed. (Freeman)

While coal reduced demand from some potential markets others developed and such was the case with the brickyards. Many a village had one since Tudor times or soon afterwards and flourished when the Georgians made brick highly fashionable, to be followed by the 19th century building boom. This was especially noticeable as the railways brought development to the last remaining wildernesses - the heathlands and many a town has an interesting story on that subject. The development on a hitherto unknown scale caused alarm with some people of which the most famous result was the founding of the National Trust.

FEEDING THE ANIMALS

As fodder Furze was of supreme importance, whether grazed on the heaths as still practised in the New Forest today, or whether it was harvested for the purpose. In severe winters when frosts scorched away any pasturage, or, when it was covered by deep snow, this was the only safe, palatable greenery available to stockmen of the heathland districts. Out they went and cut the young strong shoots springing from the stools left after the previous cutting. Continual harvesting for all purposes ensured there was a ready supply of regenerating growth. Indeed, like other heathland shrubs, the natural life-span is often less than thirty years but cutting prolongs this indefinitely. Regular harvesting of this renewable resource meant also that it was still at a manageable size and not impenetrable thickets head high. This is one of the few uses for which the Dwarf Gorse, *Ulex minor*, could be employed.

Primarily it was used as horse feed. Cattle browse regenerating shoots but when fed it as fodder they are less keen, so it was used to bulk up the rest of their feed. There is of course the problem of all those spines. Ideally young growth was used when it was spineless or while they were still soft, otherwise they had to be crushed. That's simple to say but hard to do, especially when so much was needed. Just as the size and appetite of a horse varied so did the generosity of the owner! Sometimes the quantity was reduced by adding oats or other feed. In Ireland a pannier per horse per day is recorded, with a pannier holding 21lbs. More frequent estimates range between 25-30lbs, qualified as being for a small horse. People who could afford big horses were unlikely to be dependent upon Furze.

At its simplest the spines were dealt with by crushing - by pounding the cuttings on a stone with a wooden mallet or in a wooden trough with a stone. The Irish evolved special long-handled mallets, up to four feet long for a good swing, with iron bound tapering circular heads. These had two cross blades set in the wider end, projecting beyond the head. There were also versions with iron studs in the end. Either way it was obviously hard work as it took a day to pound enough for a horse team but again records range widely, from four to eight horses, and depending whether the Furze was already cut and to hand. For cattle it had to be pulped extra soft. In Scotland they flailed it, which is not very effective, so the flails were bladed with pieces of hoop iron. It's hardly surprising that many farmers put it through the cider mill while in other places the usage was sufficient to warrant the building of special water mills, wherein wooden mallets pounded the stuff (Isle of Man) or toothed rollers tore it apart (Wales). A mill from Dolwen, Clwyd, has been rebuilt at the Welsh Folk Museum, St. Fagans, near Cardiff. They became well established by c.1800 only to be superseded by hand machines as 19th century inventiveness got under way. Some correspondents remembered putting it through the chaff-cutter and

old farming catalogues show the chaff cutter design as a furze cutter. In the records any preparation is likely to be called 'bruising' which implies that hand crushing was the first technique and that chopping, tearing, etc. evolved out of it.

The artist Thomas Bewick (born in 1753 at Ovingham, Tyneside) recalled Furze for fodder in his *Memoirs*:- *"In the early spring it was a common job for me before setting off to school to rise betimes in the morning, and eqipt with an apron, an old dyking mitten and a sharpened broken sickle to set off among the whin bushes, which were near to hand to cut off last year's sprouts. These were laid in a corner until the evening when I stript and fell to work to 'cree' them with a 'mell' in a stone trough till the tops of the whins were beaten to the consistency of soft, wet grass and with this mess I fed the horses before I went to bed..It agreed so well with them with a little oats that they soon became sleek."*

The notion of the sleek coat is reported far and wide, for over three centuries: *"The young and tender Tops of Furzes, being a little bruised, and given to a lean, sickly Horse, will strangely recover and plump him."* (Evelyn) Similarly, reports today uphold that

claim that a sickly horse fed on such tops recovers quickly. A horse off its feed can be enticed with a bundle of uncrushed Furze hung up in the stall to be nibbled. Another old notion, still upheld, says horses fed on uncrushed Furze over a length of time grow a protective moustache in defence against the sharp spines. Others assert that horses grow moustaches when kept in stalls through the winter and lose them as soon as they return to grazing, as in this early 20th century remembrance of Enstone, Oxon.:

"Most of 'em growed a moustache while they were feeding indoors for the winter, but it soon wore off once they were out at pasture, grazing again, in the spring." (Stewart, Sheila; *Lifting The Latch*; p.116)

HEALTH CARE

The nutritive value of Furze for livestock is not very great but in poor heathland communities it saved lives. This was particularly true in Ireland following the Potato Famine when root crops and hay were scarce and highly priced. For human health, Furze has not played a great part. Decoctions of the growth are astringent and have been used against diarrhoea and what Gerard called *"for staying of the laske"* which the dictionary defines as *"laxness of the bowels"*. It was used also for excessive menstrual flow and for various stones. The yellow flowers suggested it would cure yellow jaundice, which derives from the Doctrine of Signatures. It was better for worms and is still in country remedies today. A handful of the flowers was boiled, sometimes in milk, strained, and the fluid administered. This was considered mild enough for use on children but readers should consult a qualified herbalist before experimenting. Animals on the other hand were kept clear of worms if Furze was used as their fodder.

Some think it was the coarse material that scraped them clear, especially from the 'bots', which were the larvae of bot flies. The insect lays its eggs on the coat which are then licked off to hatch in the stomach and attack the wall. The presence of alkaloids such as ulexine in the Furze may have a part to play in this vermifuge action.

ROOFS AND BUILDINGS WELLS AND STACKS

Can you imagine trying to thatch a roof with Furze? There were three ways of doing it. One was to dump it on animal shelters in the fields as a primitive covering, where it probably trapped the warm rising air but wouldn't have kept out heavy rain. Secondly mature Furze bushes were fired in the spring and left for the summer rains to clean the blackened trunks ready for an autumn harvest. These were then used as roof timbers for small spans. Modern floras say the shrub grows to two metres "or more" which must have been a lot more in former times as some roof timbers have been recorded at around five metres. The shorter thinner timbers were used as the lesser horizontal roof members between the main beams to support more conventional thatch. This was sometimes developed into a woven mesh to which the thatch was sewn as per usual. Between this mesh and the thatch a layer of twiggy Furze could be placed to trap warm air and to stop dirt falling through if the roof was being covered with turves, which would be placed soil side downwards.

As for building - chopped Furze was sometimes employed as bonding material in cob walls and in plaster. In either case the stuff being chopped should not be so young that when it shrivelled it shrank and weakened the structure. Neither should it be so old as to become brittle. Otherwise the tops were used as binding material when clay was being pounded into the potholes of the highway, often by the poor heathland folk eking out a meagre living, or, in many districts, by the inmates of the workhouse.

When it came to chimneys, dragging a Furze bush down with a rope was a good way of shifting soot. If the bush was tied in the centre of the rope then it could be shunted up and down the chimney between a worker on the roof and one in the hearth. In non heathland areas Holly was used instead (until the early 1960s in Surrey). Wells were cleaned similarly but the Furze bush had to be heavily weighted to send it plunging down with enough force to scrape the sides effectively; fine going down but hard work getting it up again.

Building hay and corn stacks often began upon a foundation layer of Furze. It is said that this was to deter vermin but rats are good jumpers and a corn stack very motivating. A better reason was to improve drainage underneath to prevent a soggy wasteful bottom layer.

WORKING THE LAND

Furze, like Broom and Sweet Gale, has nodules of bacteria on its roots to put nitrogen back into the soil and so Furze was grown as a natural way of fertilizing the land. When the Furze was ripped out of the ground leaving the rootlets and nodules behind they fertilized the subsequent crop. To this end Furze was grown as an undercrop of cereals and with hay, especially if the land was destined to lie fallow the following year, allowing a crop of Furze to be harvested. Overlapping the cycles in this way was obviously sound economic sense. Countless old field maps bear the name 'Furze Field' but these should be interpreted with caution. In the absence of other evidence it will not be clear whether this records temporary or permanent usage, nor whether the name has been handed down for generations or whether it records the usage during the year of mapping. Back in the 17th century John Evelyn, through his *Silva*, was exhorting fellow landowners to use Furze not only to improve their land but as a lucrative crop. He reported *"a worthy correspondent of mine"* claimed the profit from Furze was greater than from an equal area of the best wheatland. Presumably Evelyn doubted this for he made it possible to identify his source, saying, *"If this be questioned....the Scene is within a Mile of Hereford, and proved by anniversary Experience, in the Lands, as I take it, of a Gentleman who is now one of the Burgesses for that City."*

When Furze land was returned to the plough the bigger roots or 'moots' were gathered to serve as a another type of fuel. They burn bright and cleanly and so were popular in domestic hearths and cooking ranges and lasted far into the 20th century. It is interesting that these are called 'moots' which some think derives from the Moot Court having to decide who should benefit from this occasional and valuable crop. An arguable point is still a 'moot point' today.

The Furze tops were converted into compost just as described for Bracken and they were also used as animal bedding - yes bedding! It was put down as a base layer in the stalls and covered with a thick layer of material such as Bracken, rushes or heather to insulate against the spines before a final covering of hay or straw. The dense spiny Furze in the bottom trapped air to increase the warmth in the stalls and improve drainage. When heavily soiled it was renewed, (the back end more frequently than the front) and it was then stacked, with or without layers of soil, ready to be spread on the fields. Alternatively it was thrown down in yards and lanes to be pulverised by stock and traffic. Just like Bracken it was highly favoured for potatoes.

Furze served for the final harrowing of a fine tilth into ploughland before seeding. The bushes were tied behind a draught animal and once weighted down with logs, were dragged across the field. Even when 'proper' harrows were commonplace Furze was tied underneath so thickly as to hold the tines clear of the ground for a finer tilth than with the tines alone. It saved work too since to get a good tilth with a tined harrow required working the fields twice, at right angles to each other. A hand-held branch is still good for scratching the surface for seeds requiring firm soil beneath them, such as lawn seed.

PROTECTIVE FURZE

Bee hives needed protection from the worst of the weather, especially if the heath caught the summer gales from off the sea. Recesses cut into a bank of Furze were just the place. Even the lee of a Furze hedge was better than nothing and such hedges were popular in counties like Cornwall because they would grow in defiance of salt winds. Apparently not all such hedges were left to the elements to stunt and prune for Evelyn reminded his Cornish readers not to waste clippings from their Furze hedges. He also drew attention to the value of this sort of protection as game cover, which was important right across the southern heathlands to East Anglia where the same usage was recorded by Chadwick. Similarly, Furze was cut and forced into gappy bottoms of poor hedges to control animals, whether livestock escaping or predators invading. It was buried with tree seeds, such as valuable Walnuts, to deter rodents from burrowing down and eating them and when the saplings were planted out Furze was piled around them as protection against browsing cattle and deer. Sprigs were also pushed into household gaps to keep rodents out.

Other uses included soap making from ashes as described for Bracken, wine-making from the flowers and using them to dye hen's eggs as Easter eggs, making the stems into walking sticks and hurleys for the Irish sport and laying the twiggy material in land drains. All in all, Furze has been an extremely valuable plant - so much so that the Church came to accept it as payment for tithes.

WHORTLE-BERRIES or BILBERRIES

Vaccinium myrtillus L.

What a tedious, back-breaking job is the gathering of these fruits! They were quite probably the first fruits ever harvested in Britain as evidence suggests that they were among the first flowering plants to colonise the land as the ice sheets retreated at the end of the last Ice Age. To do that in those days when there were fewer bees means they must have been better able to self-pollinate than they are today. Now they rely very much upon cross pollination by bees and by long-tongued bees at that, which are able to probe deep into the bell-shaped flowers to reach the nectar. Those early plants must have been more tolerant of severe frost too.

VALUABLE BERRIES

The little black berries give rise to over twenty names for the shrub. Bilberry is the best known and is now almost universal, while in the south east the name Whortleberry still predominates. The fruits are therefore known as whorts or hurts. They are the sole value of the plant since prolonged consumption of the leaves, whether in herbal medicine or as an adulterant in tea, has been found to produce symptoms of poisoning. They were not just used for culinary and medicinal purposes but also for brewing and dyeing.

Hurts are delicious. They have long been distilled by brewers as a flavouring of certain liqueurs while Bilberry wine has been made even more widely and been of some economic value in Central Europe. The plant has scarcely ever been grown as a commercial crop in Britain although its close relative, the larger American Blueberry (*V. corymbosum*) is being tried. Hurts have been used to colour other wines but more so on the Continent than in Britain where our traditional wine colourants have been Elderberries and Mulberries.

Dyers in the Middle Ages used all these berries, often combining them, to try to make a good blue for writing and painting. The best blue came from France as 'turnsole' but whenever relations with France were strained we had to make our own substitutes. Hurts yield a rather purplish blue but no doubt this was better than nothing when blue was one of the most important colours of all, especially in the later Middle Ages when it became the standard colour with which artists rendered the Virgin Mary's gown. Dyers maintained the use of hurts for dyeing wool, linen and paper until the development of aniline dyes in the 19th century. Britain began importing these but the First World War ended supplies from countries such as Germany. That forced a return to home-grown fruit again, much to the annoyance of the jam-makers who lost part of the important Irish Bilberry harvest to the dyers, just when cheap jam was most needed.

The hurts won favour for jam because they have smaller seeds than currants. They are also naturally sweet, needing only about a kilogram of sugar for every two kilograms of fruit. Thus they were an ideal additive to cheaper jams, apart from being full of flavour and healthy. They are rich in vitamin C and contain the required compounds from which the body makes vitamin A. Among fruits, the apricots and the elderberries are richest for vitamin A but hurts, cranberries, red currants, rose hips and Rowan berries all rank highly.

Alternatively they are splendid as fresh fruit, as any harvester will confirm. There's no point trying to eat a few without being noticed, for as Gerard noted back in the 16th century: *"these berries do colour the mouth and lips of those that eat them with a blacke colour."* The Tudors were keen on fruit and so it is no surprise to find Gerard reporting that: *"The people of Cheshire do eat the blacke Whortles in creame and milke, as in these south parts we eate Strawberries."*

To pharmacists this is 'myrtillus', valued for being astringent, antiseptic, diuretic and nutritive. For these purposes it is usually the fruits that are used. They are still official medicines in the Swiss and Austrian pharmacopoeias while the British one records use for ophthalmic disorders such as degenerative retinal conditions and against some circulatory disorders.

Hurts act as a mouth antiseptic as soon as they are eaten and have been recommended for mouth ulcers, throat ulcers, stomatitis and to arrest vomiting. They pass quickly through the stomach without affecting it and begin work in the small intestine. They act as a diuretic, removing excess liquid, and have therefore been promoted as good against diarrhoea and dysentery, but beware, that varies from person to person - in some people hurts can actually *cause* diarrhoea! The dried fruits do not pose that threat. Once in the circulation the compounds are said to be cooling, for typhoid fever etc. while acting against infections of the liver, kidneys and bladder.

out by the simple expedient of rolling the panful down a wet sloping plank: the fruit were caught in a container at the bottom while the leaves stuck to the wet wood ready to be wiped or swilt off.

The harvest was measured by volume rather than weight and so payment was by the quart. Throughout the south country the price in the early 20th century was surprisingly consistent at 4d a quart at the start of the season, dropping to 3d or even a halfpenny less. The shrubs open their flowers in succession so fruiting lasts over five or six weeks, providing a major heathland harvest. All hands were needed so schools closed. This was their 'Harvest Holiday' which in other regions would be for such work as hop or potato picking. Records of a child picking only a quart a day must surely relate to poor seasons and shaded grounds; the little berries are indeed fiddly but a bit of effort

The leaves, used professionally with due caution, reduce blood sugar levels by a weak hypoglycaemic action. They have, therefore, been employed in the treatment of diabetes, usually in conjunction with other herbs. Tea made from Whortleberry leaves has been recommended for diabetes but as with so many herbal treatments it takes time before the benefits become apparent and it is the sustained use of this herb that is questionable. Apart from that, the leaves are only available seasonally for the shrub is deciduous. The tea has also been recommended for coughs and the juice as a gargle for respiratory catarrh. Nursing mothers should note that hurts have the reputation in the countryside for reducing milk.

can fill a can quicker than that! Adults working hard got 12-28 quarts a day. Earnings from the last day's pickings by the children were, in some places, granted to the children to keep for themselves. Otherwise this seasonal bounty funded households through the winter, paying for warm clothes, extra fuel and food.

On the whole these grand little shrubs appear to have been little used by the country healers. Even in the 17th century when Nicholas Culpeper was listing its virtues he lamented that *"It is a pity they are used no more in physic than they are."* Nevertheless they do still have homeopathic uses today.

Local pickings were bought by a 'middle man' who had the services of a cart. After emptying the cans into small barrels, he carted them off for re-sale. From the south eastern heaths they went to London. Thus Gilbert White recorded in his diary on 27th June 1788 that he *"met a cartload of whortel-berries on the road"* as he travelled back to Selborne from South Lambeth. During the 18th century Surrey's great heathy hill called the Churchwood started to be known as the Hurtwood, which persists today, and that change is thought to reflect the increasing importance of the hurt trade. Mountford records Surrey hurting in the mid 1860s but by this time the demand from London must have been in decline as Johnson wrote in 1862 that,

HARVEST DAYS

On a fine breezy summer's day to be out on the heathlands gathering Hurts can be quite exhiliarating; the first tasty pickings blacken the mouth and then the back complains of the lowness of the bushes! To speed things up regular harvesters invented a 'rake' shaped like a household dust-pan but with large teeth along the front edge. With this the bushes were combed upwards so that the fruit ran back into the pan as did some of the leaves. These were separated

"in some heathy districts large quantities are collected every season and consumed by the peasantry, or sent into the towns for sale. Bilberries were thus formerly brought to London from the heaths of Surrey, and other wilds in the neighbourhood of the metropolis: but since the importation of cranberries from the Baltic they are less esteemed, and are now comparatively seldom seen in the markets."

THE BROOM-MAKERS

It was on the 15th February in 1769 that Joseph Ellis was out on Byfleet Common cutting heather from which to make brooms. Sarah Cooper was there helping. They loaded the donkey and set off along the King's Highway towards Weybridge. Sarah was some way ahead of Joseph and had to shout back to him for help when her way was suddenly blocked by two other broom-makers, Thomas and Henry Woods. It was Thomas who *"stopped the ass and threw down the heath"* by which time Joseph arrived. Thomas turned on him next and, ably assisted by Henry, *"violently beat and wounded him."* In compensation for this, the Justice of the Peace, Richard Wyatt, awarded the sum of one guinea in damages. He recorded this in his *Deposition Book*, now in the Surrey Record Office.

Therein we read that just a few weeks later, on April 5th, Thomas Woods was back in court before Wyatt. This time he was the plaintive, explaining that earlier that day he had been cutting heath on Byfleet Common when he was approached by three other broom-makers, John Southey, Thomas Young and Thomas Hummick, all from Chertsey. Forcibly, they stole eight bundles of his heath, with Hummick threatening that if Woods resisted *"he would chop him down with a hook which he had in his hand."*

People like broom-makers living off the heathland economy could have the very poorest of livings; life was tough and so were the people. Those who lived on the heath or worked from it, were known as 'heathers' (pronounced heethers) and had a reputation for uncouth language and violent behaviour. This persisted right through the 19th century and well in the 20th, becoming a epithet of insult . It was in the mid 1950s that the writer remembers his father being felled with a blow from someone he'd just called a heather. Mixing with the local heather children was not allowed. [Gypsies were mobile; heathers stayed put.]

Not all broom-makers were of this disposition of course and not all were desperately poor. Take Mr. Edward Moorey of Haslemere, Surrey, for example. He owned a house and a broom-making factory [on Clayhill Moor - now Weyhill] where he produced brooms of such quality that their fame spread to London and the mother of Queen Victoria. He delivered the brooms to Kensington Palace himself, loading them into the bottom of his donkey cart with brooms for the commoners on top and then driving to Godalming station [so from the dates of the stations this is between 1849 and 1859] where the train took them to London. Moorey and his donkey followed by road [2 days]. His grandson remembered *'Broom Maker to Her Majesty the Queen'* painted on the side of the cart.

[see *The Broom Squires of Hindhead*, Christine Herring]

This reputation for quality must have been hard-earned as the 1851 census records no less than twenty five broom-makers on that western (heathland) side of Haslemere alone. Moorey is there, listed with brother-in-law William Madgewick and his two brothers John and James Madgewick. He was then aged thirty five and had been born in the county at Frensham. So had fourteen of the others. Frensham, with its extensive heath, appears to have been a great training ground for broom-makers but by this time they had all moved out into the surrounding villages.

George Boxall was another. He married Mary from Lurgashall over the Sussex border but within two years of the birth of their fifth child they left Frensham for the Devil's Punch Bowl. They took with them another Boxall, James, aged 27 as servant and broom-maker and the business was also able to fund the education of Boxall's four older children plus the wages of David Windybank from Sheet over the Hampshire border. They were one of seven households listed in the Punch Bowl, of which two others were broom-makers. Both were William Snellings, presumably father and son, as the elder was 78 but still listed as broom-maker, while the other was 41. He was doing well enough to support a wife and six children. The eldest, James, aged 18, had started broom-making but the next three were all incurring the expense of being educated. Clearly not all broom- makers were at the lowest social level, although this community probably became that by the time it was depicted by the local vicar, S. Baring-Gould (who recorded so much of country life) in his romantic novel, *The Broom-Squire* (Methuen 1913). That vivid tale is surprisingly scant in descriptive detail; the *"rattle-trap farmhouse, built partly of brick, mainly of timber, thatched with heather"* survives today, now tiled and less rattle-trap. One of the poorer homes survives as the Youth Hostel but the rest have now all but disappeared, although the ruins of the community were clear enough to be mapped by the writer in 1964.

There were once hundreds and hundreds of such families employed as broom-makers, known also as broom-squarers or broom-squires in some places while in others they were broom-dashers or bashers. In the days before vacuum cleaners there was a huge demand for brooms and brushes for domestic use in both town and country. There were also important demands from industry and for services that are mechanised today, such as street cleaning. When Mr. Moorey took his brooms into London he was perpetuating an old tradition. By the early Middle Ages civic pride was demanding clean streets, not just in London but the other urban centres in the realm. Generally town authorities, such as for London and Bristol, ordained that it was the responsibility of the householder to ensure that the street was kept clean within the width of his own frontage. Frequently an officer was appointed to check this and upon a particular day - Saturday in both Coventry and Ipswich. Any defaulters in Coventry (1421) were fined 12d. There was a massive fine of 6s 8d in Chester (1384) for anyone who cleared his stretch by dumping his muck in his neighbour's frontage! This was a common ploy everywhere and anyone getting caught was likely to claim that the rain had washed it there! The authorities at Coventry lost patience with this and forbade any man from raking or sweeping across the frontages when it was raining. Some authorities initiated the occupation of road-sweeper and some also provided a cart. Certainly there was a lot to clear. Excrement, from both humans and livestock, was the greatest problem but butchers dumped their offal in the streets, while everyone's dead animals, even as big as horses, were just abandoned there. Industrial waste piled up too, ranging from carpenters' shavings to the very unpopular stinking swill from the dyers.

[see Salusbury].

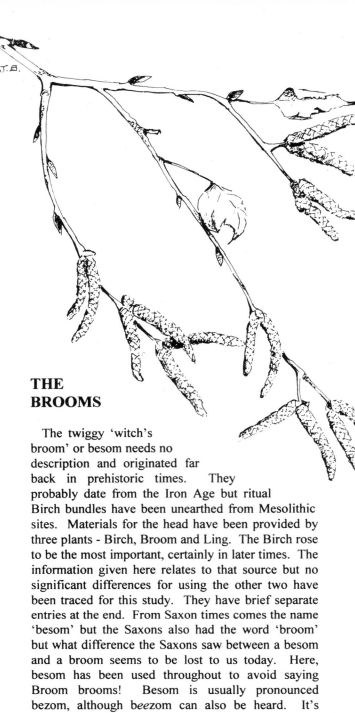

THE BROOMS

The twiggy 'witch's broom' or besom needs no description and originated far back in prehistoric times. They probably date from the Iron Age but ritual Birch bundles have been unearthed from Mesolithic sites. Materials for the head have been provided by three plants - Birch, Broom and Ling. The Birch rose to be the most important, certainly in later times. The information given here relates to that source but no significant differences for using the other two have been traced for this study. They have brief separate entries at the end. From Saxon times comes the name 'besom' but the Saxons also had the word 'broom' but what difference the Saxons saw between a besom and a broom seems to be lost to us today. Here, besom has been used throughout to avoid saying Broom brooms! Besom is usually pronounced bezom, although beezom can also be heard. It's nothing more than a bundle of twigs bound round a handle but a well-made one is a work of craftsmanship. It will be highly serviceable when used appropriately. Some of those on sale in garden centres etc. today are appalling and a great insult to the true craftsman.

A besom broom should be long and springy with the twigs lying close together without side shoots sticking out to snag into everything nearby. Their versality can be demonstrated through their use in large gardens in later times where they were used firstly by the lawnsman to swish the dew off the grass prior to mowing. This was achieved with a light touch, at a low angle, using the hip for leverage. As the twigs wore down the besom passed on to destroying worm casts in the grass. It was a lawnsman's sin to flatten with the mower roller a worm cast into an ugly brown splat Next, when thus worn down a bit more, it flicked off the autumn leaves. Then it went into general garden use, such as shifting autumn leaves off harder surfaces which soon wore it down to being efficient at scarifying moss, algae and winter ice off the paths and drives, until the stems were down to the stumps and then they worked at snow. After that it still wasn't useless but kept until the following summer for igniting and ramming into wasp nests.

THE RAW MATERIALS

Cutting Birch for the heads was winter work when the twigs were bare, running into early spring, before the buds began to split. The writer remembers leafy twigs being used fresh when a particularly springy besom was needed, as on bowling greens, but such brooms seem to have been a rarity, judging by the records. The best came from coppice stools as these shoot up long and straight without many awkward spreading side shoots, when the stools are close-grown. A second option was to strip the twigs off boughs of older trees before the tips turn pendulous but it is much more difficult then to cut enough that is three or more feet long with few woody side spreaders. There are many regional names for this twiggy material, such as spray, bish, trash, ricings.

The broom-maker took this back to his yard to be stacked in bundles. Each bundle had enough for six besoms and each besom took a full double handful of stems and each stem was no more than three eighths of an inch thick. The bottom layer of the stack was raised off the ground for good drainage and to let the air circulate. The succeeding layers were laid contrarywise to the previous. The weight compressed the spray and as it seasoned so it hardened in this desired straightness. Leave it too long and it would become too brittle. Six months was usually the limit. No doubt housewives and servants in doorways became adept at recognising a good broom when they saw one with many an argument arising over the price!

The handles or 'tails' would have to be bought in, except on heaths where older Birch poles were big enough to use. Hazel rods from the coppice workers were preferred for purchase, although Ash was smoothest of all and could look very smart. Ash was often more expensive and some said too heavy. For lightness and cheapness, many areas offered Willow but these can become too brittle too quickly. Lime and Sycamore were also used where available. Poles were about one and a half inches in diameter and some three and half feet long, when trimmed, so that when driven into the head they give an overall length of besom of five feet. Some broom-makers varied this to suit their regular customers as some did with the size of the head - that double handful being varied between ten and twelve inch diameter options.

Like the spray, the poles for tails were stacked, in the shade, waiting to be used, preferably within six months again.

Thirdly, material for 'bonds' was needed - the material that bound the head so tightly together that it didn't fall apart when sweeping. Before the days of soft wire, Brambles were judged the best. Long suckers were cut and stripped of their bark and thorns by ripping the stem between two closely driven nails, preferably when wearing leather gloves. Then the clean white stem was split with a knife and levered into two. Some craftsmen removed the central pith by bending the stem backwards to force the pith upwards for cleaning away with the knife. These riven stems are then ready to use but only on besoms for immediate use as Bramble bonds loose their strength in a month or less. Occupations that involved sweeping round fires used these as the tips of the head burnt down rapidly in the hot ashes anyway.

More durable than Brambles were strips of Ash, Chestnut, Hazel or Oak, bought where available but usually from the coppice workers. They were converted into bonds in much the same way, although Hazel often needed extra care when splitting to ensure an even thickness. Ash was deemed the most beautiful, for its smart whiteness, and craftsmen had a keen eye for a good finish however mundane the task. Rods about an inch in diameter and four feet long were left to harden for a few weeks and then split into three with a triangular wedge (made of Box or Holly) and the pith is removed. These are riven down to strips, sometimes as little as a sixteenth of an inch thick, but which have all the strength and durability required. They are used as soon as they are made.

TEAM WORK

Where the broom-making was a small family business then the wife worked at it too. If the Birch was rough-cut, especially from trees rather than coppice stools, it was brought back to the yard where the wife, with her experience, sorted and trimmed it to the correct length. Then she and maybe her daughters made up the faggot bundles and stacked them. Later their task was to 'break birch' when they unloaded the faggots of spray from the seasoning stack and broke them open ready for the husband to work up into besoms. Children prepared bonds at the same time, by working them in a pail of water to get the strips supple. Gertrude Jekyll noted, *"There is usually a little pool of water near the broom-maker's shed, where the bonds are soaked,"* but this should not be taken as an overall rule. There was as much variation across the country in this craft as any other.

Making the broom, sitting astride a special wooden 'horse' was the man's work. The horse had a clamp that was opened or closed by a foot lever and into this clamp was held the end of the bond while under it, and across the horse was gathered the spray. The bundle was gathered tightly and then pulled even tighter by rotation against the bond to bind it round. This was done three times for Birch but only twice for the smaller Ling brooms. There was an intricate and variable way of linking the binding rings without cutting the bond and then for driving the end of the bond into the head so as it remained totally secure. The tail was sometimes in place from the start, in which case pegs were driven through the head between the bonds into drilled holes in the tail to help hold on the head, or, the tail was driven into the head at the end, thereby taking up any final slack. To drive the tail into the head was a simple matter of upending the broom into a vertical position with the tail loosely fitted and banging the tail down smartly onto a hard surface. The impact drew the head down around the tail.

Finally there was the task of selling them on. Some were lucky enough to be able to hire a farmer's hay wain or other large waggon to go off for weeks touring markets, fairs, workplaces and homes, looking for customers. Others had to make do with a donkey cart. Fathers and older sons could be gone for weeks, travelling from county to county.

Ling besom back in use:
Oakhurst Cottage, Hambledon,
Surrey, in the care of the
National Trust; furnished as
per c.1850.

HEATHER BESOMS

Ling besoms were primarily for indoor use, being less abrasive than Birch. At the very beginning of the 20th century both were still in demand and respected, even by middle class householders like Gertrude Jekyll. She commented in 1904 that, *"As no cast-iron or machine-made substitute for these useful things has yet appeared, let us hope that they may still remain."* That was barely true; Victorian catalogues reveal how the industrialists had designed and marketed a vast proliferation of specialist brushes and brooms for every conceivable nook and cranny where even a single dust mote might settle. Nevertheless she paid her half crown and got a dozen of what she wanted.

Ling for besoms was cut in the early spring when it was green and pliant. This was as early as February and March in those districts where the heather provided nesting sites for valued game birds, so as to avoid disturbing them. Both the birds and the broom-maker wanted the Ling two to three feet high. In other words, areas of Ling must have been set aside for these purposes since grazing and turf-cutting would have kept it very short.

Cutting it so early meant it was more serviceable since it was less prone to shed leaves and bits of bark. It was stacked to compress and dry as per Birch and then made up in the same way later in the spring and through the summer. Particular care had to be taken with the stacking to ensure that air really did circulate as Ling traps more moisture than Birch and nobody wanted a mouldy broom. Each bundle in the stack was enough to make six besoms.

A survey of 1796 recorded, *"All the tenants in the area use unlimited rights on the very extensive commons and heaths which have poor herbage for cattle but heath much used for broom-making."*
(ref. Potters Park Farm and estate, Surrey, quoted by Stratton)

BROOM

Making besoms from Broom, *Cytisus scoparius*, is very little recorded, even though the practice was so important that it gave its name to the plant. Even the botanical name *scoparius* comes from the Latin *scopa* for a broom and when it was formerly in the genus *Sarothamnus* the name came from the two Greek words meaning to sweep and a shrub.

The material harvested would have been the young green growth for as Broom stems mature they harden and become rigid. Once they have been cut and dried they become brittle. For this reason it was presumably made into brooms and sold straight away rather than stacking and drying it. Further searches through local records might throw some light upon this. Certainly references to Broom are often to *green* Broom, as in the proverb from the 16th century: *The green new broom sweepeth clean."*

Further, there are widespread taboos through the southern counties from Devon to Sussex, Berkshire to Suffolk, against sweeping the house in May with *blossomed* Broom, showing it was used fresh:

*Sweep the house with blossomed broom in May
And you'll sweep the head of the house away.*

Even bringing the blossom indoors was an ill omen of death although in Devon, at least, it was used to decorate the churches for spring weddings. Any ill meaning was obviously overcome by its nature as a fertility plant from ancient cultures. From the viewpoint of the broom-maker these taboos presumably interrupted his retailing throughout May. In Devon the same taboos covered Ling besoms too so he must have been glad of Birch ones to offer instead. At least Birch was considered protective!

There are several references to Broom making the best besoms of all but that of course depends upon the purpose of the sweeping. Did it once have a particular use which was lost at an early date? When the woollen industry sheered the cloth on the racks to get an even nap what did they use to sweep off the sheerings without snagging up the cloth? Switches of fresh Broom with their soft tips would do that very nicely wouldn't they? Otherwise, as late as 1904, Getrude Jekyll recorded the favour with which these brooms were viewed by the country folk who asserted they were best of all for bringing up the redness of brick floors and paths. When tested for this study that proved to be true, after repeated brushings. It has been suggested that this is due to the Broom storing crystals of alkaline calcium in its twigs, which during brushing, are smeared over the acid coating of algae. It kills the algae to reveal the smart red brick beneath.

By making besoms I win my bread,
And spindles and whorls in times o need;
Isn't that a gentle trade indeed?
Bonnie lassie, can you loe me?   (loe/love)

Stanza 7 from *The Beggar Laddie*,
(see Child, vol.V, 119)

Brooms were carried on the shoulder, heads and tails interlocked in pairs, three deep, to make twelve and then a thirteenth on top. Brooms were often sold in 'dozens' of thirteen but does any reader know why there were thirteen in a broom-maker's dozen?

HEATHLAND PEOPLE AND THEIR HOMES

Through the foregoing plant portraits all manner of people have been introduced from all classes of society, either earning their living directly off the heaths or by using raw materials gathered and sometimes processed there, through to people in distant places using soap and brooms, jams and dyes etc. The first group, who worked and lived on the heaths, were usually considered to be at the bottom of the social scale. Even their faith in God was questioned. These are the original pagans. The Romans used the Latin word *pagus* for a village and it came to mean a villager or a peasant and by the time of the Caesars it was a term of contempt for rural civilians as opposed to the trained, disciplined soldiers. Once the military centres had been converted to Christianity then the people were 'soldiers of Christ' and those out in the country were definitely *pagans*. The heathland people were the last great group to be converted, so to the Scandinavian and Germanic tribes they were associated with heather. The ancient names for this gave rise to the German *der Heide* for heather, and, by changing the gender, *die Heide*, for pagan or *heathen*.

Many of their ancient practices, in terms of plant usage, have come down to us today and have been recorded in this book, leaving a little space in which to record the sort of homes we should imagine as the setting for their family life of the people at the lower end of the social scale. They will not be found in the standard architecture books. They were, at best, of wattle and daub panels, the same as other early 'peasant' homes. On the heathlands they had an alternative. The walls could be made of stacked heather turves, and these were still in use in the 19th century. Turf walls offered fewer draughts and greater insulation than the wattle and daub but could not be raised to a great height so these homes would be called bungalows today.

The roof rafters were Furze stems, which, not being of great length, required the homes to be narrow. For thatch there was heather turf and sometimes Bracken or even Furze. It could be difficult to get an adequate pitch to the roof, for shedding water, if the walls were of turf, especially if the roof was stretched from side to side without a ridge. To overcome this, some homes had a few poor quality timbers to create gable ends and the ridge. Others used stone, or later, brick, for the ends. In later times a substantial hearth, oven and chimney were built of brick or stone and the rest of the home was practically a lean-to against it. Earlier, the hearth was in the centre of the floor, where it could not ignite the turf walls but even so there was little space to move around inside. One such home was recorded as being eight feet by twelve feet inside.

Where available, clay was used for the walls. Such 'cob' walls are a West Country speciality today but were formerly widespread. Hersham in Surrey had such a community, known as Mud Town, until some of the homes suffered bomb damage in the Second World War and the rest were demolished soon after.

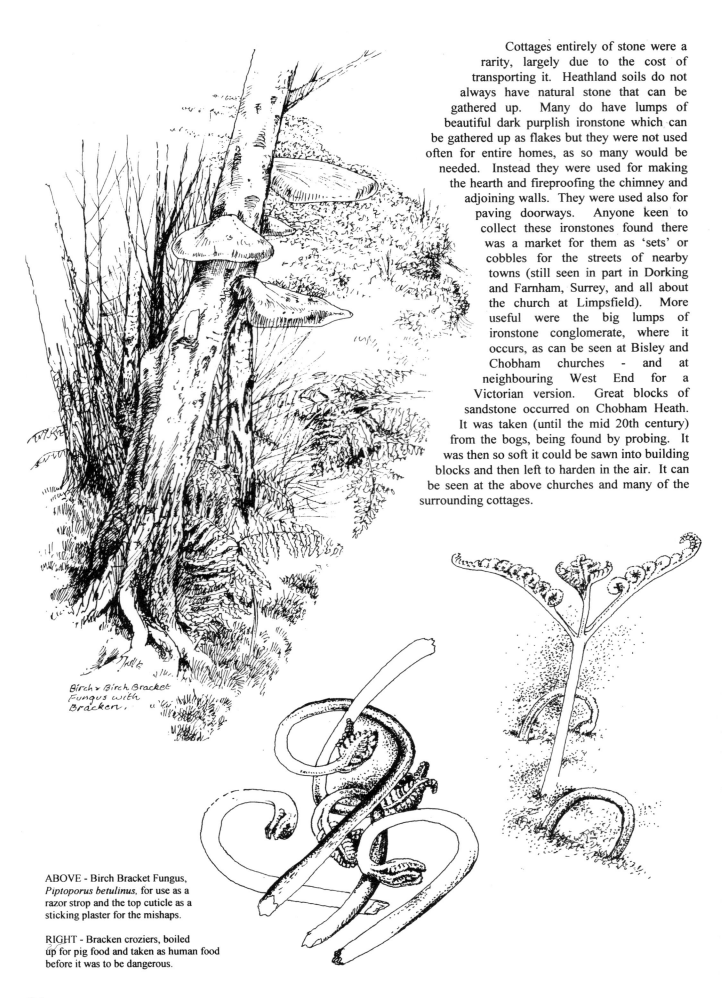

Cottages entirely of stone were a rarity, largely due to the cost of transporting it. Heathland soils do not always have natural stone that can be gathered up. Many do have lumps of beautiful dark purplish ironstone which can be gathered up as flakes but they were not used often for entire homes, as so many would be needed. Instead they were used for making the hearth and fireproofing the chimney and adjoining walls. They were used also for paving doorways. Anyone keen to collect these ironstones found there was a market for them as 'sets' or cobbles for the streets of nearby towns (still seen in part in Dorking and Farnham, Surrey, and all about the church at Limpsfield). More useful were the big lumps of ironstone conglomerate, where it occurs, as can be seen at Bisley and Chobham churches - and at neighbouring West End for a Victorian version. Great blocks of sandstone occurred on Chobham Heath. It was taken (until the mid 20th century) from the bogs, being found by probing. It was then so soft it could be sawn into building blocks and then left to harden in the air. It can be seen at the above churches and many of the surrounding cottages.

Birch & Birch Bracket Fungus with Bracken.

ABOVE - Birch Bracket Fungus, *Piptoporus betulinus*, for use as a razor strop and the top cuticle as a sticking plaster for the mishaps.

RIGHT - Bracken croziers, boiled up for pig food and taken as human food before it was to be dangerous.

The door into the homes was a wattle panel or else sacking was hung up. Inside, the floor was dry clean sand. Selling sand, to be used as a scouring agent, was another source of income for the heathlanders and many readers will remember that as children they had to be asleep before the sand-man came or else he would sprinkle sand in their eyes! The sand-man came in the evening when the women were back from the fields. The last thing mothers wanted to be doing was getting children to sleep for had not the sand-man been round all the neighbours and gathered all the gossip!

The homes were warmed (not heated) by a fire of turves. Smoke often had to drift out of the doorway as there was not always a chimney or smoke hole, nor glazed windows, as glass was very expensive. Wooden shutters or sacking served instead when the weather was bad. There was very little furniture and even the bed could hardly be described as furniture. It was not a carpenter's masterpiece so much as a heap, across one end, but one made carefully nevertheless. There was a bottom layer of coarse twigs or Furze to allow air to circulate and urine to drain through. Then there was the main 'mattress' of springy Ling tied in bundles and stacked contrariwise in layers. Over this was, hopefully, a soft layer of hay or Purple Moor Grass in a coarse sacking bag but Beech or Sweet Chestnut leaves were deemed best. Bed 'linen' might be linen if it could be home grown but otherwise it was likely to be hemp sacking. Until later times the whole family slept here together.

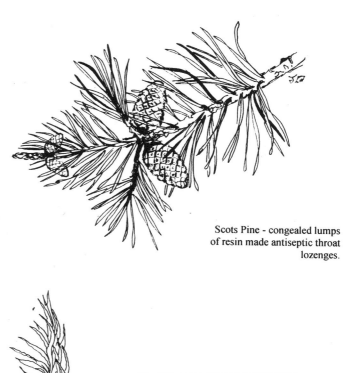

Scots Pine - congealed lumps of resin made antiseptic throat lozenges.

The little moss, *Dicranum scoparium*, used for shaving brushes as they kept their softness and did not shed their leaves, after drying.

The other vital furnishing was the cooking pot. That kept warm on the turf fire but had to be brought to the boil using 'hurriers' such as dried Bracken or Birch twigs. Thus the hearth and its pot were the focal point of family life; the scene of cooking, brewing, dyeing and preparing medicines, using the heathland plants. Efforts to conserve those plants today is reviving old practices, such as grazing the heaths, which is the final topic....

Sphagnum

GRASSES AND GRAZING

Vast flocks of sheep once grazed the heathlands. The village cattle were put out there too. Horses and ponies, donkeys and mules, goats and poultry added to the scene. Trees didn't get a chance. The main grazing was not grass but the shrubs, primarily Ling. This is how it had always been, since prehistoric times, when it is thought that the first herdsmen cleared woodland and scrub to increase the grazing. Grasses and 'weeds' no doubt shot up first but over-grazing caused the soils to deteriorate and give rise to what are now called heathlands. Modern archaeology is adjusting this story locally and nationally.

courts by those villagers entitled to do so. Such entitlements have come down to us as part of 'commoners' rights' and give rise to so many heaths being called 'commons'. Despite attempts by governments to extinguish such rights in the 20th century some survive and are practised. The most famous of these, for southern heathlands, are for the New Forest where the practice has lasted over 900 years, making it unique in Europe. Being a former royal forest these lands were administered by the Crown for the Crown, by officers called 'verderers' (from the Latin for green as in verdure for green pasture). These people and their courts are well documented elsewhere.

Today, the need to conserve this rare habitat in a cost-effective and sustainable way has led to the reintroduction of grazing onto some heaths. Initial experiments were encouraging, and as people re-learned what our ancestors knew, so the schemes are becoming more successful and more numerous. Taking the children to see the animals on the heath is becoming an attractive alternative to feeding the ducks on the village pond. They can enjoy something that has not been seen on the heath for perhaps thirty, sixty, or more years. National Trust officers and Council Officials alike are learning to work as would a Tudor 'husbandman'.

These grazings were vital. Villages were rare on heathland due to shortage of water and the poorness of the soils for growing crops. Communities developed down on the spring line or along any rivers that cut through the heathlands (which shows up very clearly in Dorset). They used their limited but better soils for cropping and utilized the surrounding heaths for grazing. The details of this usage and its administration will depend upon the histories of the individual heaths and upon the period in time being reviewed. No land was 'no man's land' - all of it was owned and that inevitably led to both permissive and restrictive regulation as to its usage. Some, even if only in part, would have been grazed on behalf of the Lord of the Manor to the exclusion of all else. Others were grazed under the supervision of the manorial

Visits to such grazing sites can be as exciting as a safari park, if you appreciate what you are seeing, for increasingly the breeds employed are rare ones. Although modern breeds would be cheaper to buy and, in some instances, more manageable, they do not prosper on heathland vegetation. Their tough constitutions have been bred out of them. Fortunately, in Britain we still have small numbers of ancient breeds, such as the Scottish Highland Cattle. These were imported by the Dutch when their modern breeds failed to come up to expectation and soon the Highlanders were munching away very satisfactorily, just as they do on Hampshire heathland and for the National Trust in the Devil's Punch Bowl. The Berkshire Heathland Project tried the ancient White Park Cattle but these lived up to their very wild reputations and so were changed to the British Whites. As for sheep, these are more difficult on the heathlands because they need shepherding to control them in the open spaces. They are better in parks and other enclosed spaces such as grasslands around reservoirs.

The ancient Soay Sheep have been tried but proved particularly difficult to control as they are most prone to escape and then they disperse, as they do not flock naturally. The Hebridean is preferred instead. The New Forest Ponies are an obvious choice and prove their worth where Purple Moor Grass needed controlling. The Exmoor Pony can be found too and the famous Longhorn cattle. They work well which all sounds too good to be true but wherever grazing is reintroduced to the heaths there is a need for fencing, for the safety of both people and livestock; to keep animals from straying in front of traffic on adjacent roads, or from straying into neighbouring gardens and so forth.

Any suggestion of fencing can fire opposition from people who use the heaths for riding, dog walking, and personal recreation. Even with public access points through the fencing they feel their rights of free access are being infringed, yet without conservation measures they will lose the open spaces they enjoy so much. They will become impenetrable thickets of Birch and Pine and Rhododendron that will curtail their free access far more and destroy the sense of open space that is otherwise so precious in many of the heathland districts - apart from accelerating the extinction of rare species of heathland wildlife.

Using rare breeds for habitat conservation is promoting the conservation of the breeds too. This is vital anyway, so that their genes can be bred back into modern stock to renew their vigour or change their characteristics. This is particularly important for the cattle and isn't just a notion - it's being done.

There have been a number of detailed studies of livestock feeding habits on sites where the tradition has not been broken, primarily the New Forest. From these we know, that cattle spend about about 60% of their time feeding because they are ruminants and so by 'chewing the cud' they extract more nutrient from a lower intake than do the non-ruminant ponies which have to feed for as much as 88% of their time due to the high throughput of food. Additionally, ponies take more woody material than cattle and so there is a higher proportion of fibre in their diet. Despite this, cattle take twice as much Ling as ponies (about 20% of their diet) but neither take Bell Heather or Cross-leaved Heath. Both take Purple Moor Grass, up to some 75% of their diet. Ponies fare better than cattle when it comes to the lawn forming grasses because they have large incisor teeth which enable them to crop the grasses shorter. Obviously these statistics demand a wide range of plants from which to graze and browse but the mixture of heathland types in the New Forest provides just that.

THE PONIES

For this study the Exmoor and New Forest Ponies were reviewed and are noted briefly here for general interest. They have a tough life on the heathlands, especially during the winters but some breeds were here at the end of the last Ice Age and still have the ability to survive snow and rain and coarse feed. The Exmoor Ponies are among the oldest, with fossils going back 100,000 years, and remain one of the hardiest of Britain's nine native breeds of pony. They have a very thick undercoat to trap the body heat and so efficient is this that warmth does not escape through to melt snow on the overcoat of the pony's back. The overcoat is of long guard hairs, waterproofed with oil, that are drawn together by rain to form triangles that shed the water from the downward points. The eyes are set under a fleshy ridge (toad-eye) which shelters them from driving rain and biting winds. So with head down away from the wind and thus protected by the body, and with the rear turned into the wind but protected by the thick tail, they survive whatever the weather throws at them. The foal (never twins) is born early, in April or early May, so it has chance to mature sufficiently to withstand its first winter. The mare is ready to mate again nine days after birth.

Despite the rigours the Exmoor Ponies have a life-span of 25-30 years. The mares stand 127cm high to the top of the shoulder while the stallion at 130cm is slightly larger. It is not known how long these small ponies have been centred upon Exmoor but breeds historian, Sylvia Calmady-Hamlyn, believed that they, and the Dartmoor Ponies, were

driven to their respective uplands from Eastern England in Saxon times.

The New Forest Ponies have probably been in their locality for some 3,000 years. Their existence was recorded by the Saxons in the early 11th century and in the next century they became the property of the local people, so establishing their place in the commoners' grazing rights. Since the 13th century there has been selective culling of weak and unworthy ponies so the breed has remained strong. Over the last 250 years, in common with the Dartmoors and other breeds, there has been a lot of hybridizing to get 'improvements' to suit different needs, such as for children's riding ponies, but the original breed still survives. It is another tough one, although the foals are born a little later than the Exmoors, in May and June, but in the New Forest winters the herds can shelter from the worst of the weather by retreating to the wooded areas. Here they change their diet from grass and Furze to such favourites as Holly and Brambles. The purest of the breed survive best.

New Forest Ponies are a little larger than the Exmoors and are divided into two grades. Those standing up to 132cm are classified as Type A while

Type B can be up to 10cm taller, at the top of the shoulder. They do not live so long as the Exmoors either (18-20 years) and do not breed so well - after foaling the mares nurture their foals and build up their own reserves for the winter and do not conceive until the following summer or the one following that.

THE CATTLE

Several organisations, including the Berkshire Heathland Project, are trying the Longhorn. This a breed of beautiful creatures, ranging in colour from light roan through to a dark plum-brindle but always with white markings. In particular they have a pale or white stripe right down their backs which may begin high up the neck. This is the crucial 'finching' or 'eelstripe' and highlights the antiquity of the breed. This is the mark borne by the ancient wild aurochsen cattle from which today's cattle are believed to have descended. Only two other breeds in Britain retain this mark of antiquity - the Gloucester, of Double Gloucester Cheese fame, and the Irish Moyled from Ulster.

The Longhorn was developed in the Craven district of Yorkshire and spread through the Lake District into Cumbria and south into the Midlands. There it was taken up by Robert Bakewell of Leicestershire as part of his famous programme of selective breeding in

"God sendeth an evil willed cow short horns."
Sir G. Bowes, 1569

the mid 18th century. (Other breeders had begun such work earlier than Bakewell). The industrialisation of the Midlands created a greater demand for meat and meat products (such as fat that made good tallow) and the Longhorn, being such a large animal was chosen as part of the programme to increase meat and meat quality. Bakewell actually reduced its size and bone weight of the Longhorn. He also played a large part in changing multi-purpose breeds into single or sometimes dual purpose. The Longhorn had been the most popular breed in the 18th century, favoured for three qualities: meat from its large carcass, milk that was rich and made good butter and, thirdly, large size and strength that suited the need for draught animals when oxen were preferred to horses, and oxen were still in use in the 20th century. Thus Longhorns became the first of the modern improved breeds, for beef, but in putting the emphasis upon size and fat so the dairying strain was lost. It was overtaken by the Shorthorn, being more successfully improved at the time.

They certainly are large animals but their most striking characteristic is their horns. They are indeed long and are wonderfully curved but not always symmetrically. They can curve out of the head at differing angles and even in differing directions. To the romantic they give 'character' and for many people this is what 'real' cattle should look like. Some modern breeding programmes reworking the

Longhorn genes are breeding out the horns (for safety). Purests will ensure we can still enjoy Longhorns for being just that. Hopefully the light red and golden colour ranges will be kept too as breeders have been favouring the darkest colouring. The future of the breed certainly got a boost in 1981 when the top beef prize at the Royal Show was won by a Longhorn.

For a while the Berkshire Heathland Project tried some of the ancient White Park Cattle but these are famed for their natural wildness and these were no exception. They were changed for a smaller type, without horns. These are British Whites which were formerly considered a strain of the White Parks until it was realised that they were a separate breed with different origins and so, since 1948, have been registered in their own separate herd book with their own name of British Whites (except in the USA where they are still called White Park). Their whiteness is highlighted by smart coloured markings, usually black but sometimes red, on the muzzle, eye-lids, teats and the fronts of their fetlocks. The dark teats have made them increasingly popular in hotter, sunnier countries such as Australia and America because they do not get sunburnt. The dark eye tissue is resistant to cancer too.

British Whites were popular in mid-Lancashire and then in East Anglia and were dual purpose cattle. Then selective breeding began to favour the dairying side but now it's going back to beef production. The cows are also proving good for suckling beef calves. This is one of our rare breeds that will soon be too popular to be rare at all and appears to have a good future.

89

THE GRASSES

There has always been more to heathland than vast areas dominated by heathers. Indeed the word 'heathland' is used frequently to describe areas of bogs and other wetlands, Furze thickets, Bracken stands, and grasslands on richer soils, which are all found within a matrix of Ling heath. There are relatively few grasses in Britain (about 152 plus some newly established aliens) and, while several can be found on grasslands on richer soils within the heathland areas, relatively few are adapted to the acid, infertile and inhospitable conditions of the heath and mire.

Of the common perennial grasses, Sheep's Fescue (*Festuca ovina*) is the grass most likely to withstand the arid conditions of the dry heath in the east of the country. For damper conditions there's Wavy Hair Grass (*Deschampsia flexuosa*) and also, but only in the western half of southern Britain, the Bristle Bent (*Agrostis curtisii*). For the wettest conditions there can be an abundance of Purple Moor Grass (*Molinia*

caerulea). Indeed there can be an over-abundance of this last species, to the detriment of other species being actively conserved today and so it has become a target for some of the recent reintroductions of grazing.

We may be getting a poor view of the grasses today, since there have been periods when the climate has been wetter and there were once many square miles of heathland that had better soils but which have since fallen to the plough or to building development. Nevertheless, descriptions from the 19th century of great golden patches of Biting Stonecrop (*Sedum acre*) mixed with bright red Sheep Sorrel (*Rumex acetosella*) on Hindhead Common, Surrey, suggest that bare spaces were not being colonised very readily by grasses at that time at least.

Much information about past patterns of vegetation is derived from identifying pollen grains preserved in wet peat. This must, however, be viewed with care since grazing off the emerging flowering stems would reduce severely the quantities of pollen produced and thereby give a false impression of the frequency of certain species. This could be of particular significance where cattle had been grazing since their manner of foraging is to wrap their tongues round the grass and tear it off. In other words the grass has to be long enough to enable this and for some species that means the flowering stems. Such treatment requires the grasses to be firmly rooted which might not be so in areas of looser sand. Similarly, sheep clamp the grass blades against their toothless upper front gum with the bottom gum and tug, so that the grass is cut against the teeth in the bottom jaw. Loose plants could be tugged out of the ground. Under these conditions and with their flowering reduced, some grases would be slow to establish when numbers of grazing animals were high.

The Sheep's Fescue is one of the species that does become firmly rooted and mat forming and as it will grow where others won't it becomes an important fodder grass. Sheep find it quite nutritious. It takes a lot of energy to graze off a mouthful of such fine leaves so livestock tend to leave it if there is anything better available. The leaves are so fine because they roll back on themselves to entrap the breathing holes in the under surface and thereby conserve moisture. It's a fineness exploited by man for quality lawns and bowling greens.

The Purple Moor Grass develops into great tussocks and any gardener who has the variegated form and tried to move an established one will know just how well it is rooted. These tussocks are a survival strategy. The grass is the only British one to be deciduous and so it needs reserves of food to start it into growth each spring. The leaves divide at the base and the stems swell with the stored food - a strategem that is also unique among British grasses. Being deciduous it changes colour in the autumn, and produces grand swathes of gold which, with the brighter yellow of the Birches, gives the wet heath a glorious final fling at the end of the season. Then it fades away, literally, as it turns nearly white and gives another colour phase to the countryside. These dead blades pull away easily in the hand, and the wind, and were gathered as animal bedding. As this harvest needs no cutting it was often the childrens' job to go out and scrape up sackfuls of the stuff. It was a harvest that was only possible where there was no grazing.

The Purple Moor Grass has a short growing season, from May to September, and it's the tall flowering stems that contribute greatly to the autumn gold. When in bloom they are far less conspicuous but have a dull purple colouring that gives the grass its name. For sheer beauty of flower the Wavy Hair Grass is unsurpassed on the heaths. Its massed delicate blooms almost shine in the sunlight and shimmer like ruffled silk in the slightest breeze. Look closely at the main stem between the flowers and there you'll find the wiggle that puts the 'wavy' into the name. Although not the most wonderful of grasses for grazing, it is important for often being abundant where other grasses won't grow; it tolerates a wide range of soils, altitudes, climate and its range stretches from Cornwall right up to the Shetland islands.

Although it provides grazing on the heathlands it has not been an important grass commercially. However, early in the 20th century it got a bad name when unscrupulous seed merchants used it to adulterate supplies of Yellow Oat-grass, *Trisetum flavescens*. The latter was an expensive seed which had poor germination so to make the return seem worth the outlay the Wavy Hair Grass was popped in to make it look good.

Today, conditions have changed on many of our heaths and species such as Wavy Hair Grass and Purple Moor Grass are on the increase. Part of this is due to the long years of neglect which have allowed decaying vegetation to accumulate, making the soils more fertile. Additionally, there is evidence that rain coming down through atmospheric pollution is absorbing nitrogen compounds, turning itself into a liquid nitrogen fertiliser. This retards some species such as Sundews but promotes grasses, thereby enabling them to outgrow heathers and other plants. One way to put the clock back is to strip off the turf mechanically to leave the bare infertile sand to recolonise slowly in the traditional way, but another, more sensitive, way is to bring back grazing and allow the animals to reduce gradually the dominance

HARVEST MOUSE threatened with extinction by combine harvesters, is moving from the corn into Purple Moor Grass, in some localities.

THE HEATHLAND SCENES

Much of the history of the livestock is documented but we know far less about the common people and their practices that enabled heathlands to be grazed at all. There was always something to do. If we could flip back through the pages of time we would see members of the poorest and smallest heathland communities carrying out drinking water in yoked pails as they tended their few beasts daily. We'd see larger herds and flocks being driven down to a water supply at regular intervals, and sometimes being left in the corn stubble overnight to eat the weeds. We'd see the milking of sheep and cows out on the heath itself and the milk being packhorsed back. There were seasonal tasks too, such as rounding up for branding, washing sheep ready for shearing and the shearing itself, out on the heaths which was also the setting for calving, foaling and lambing.

There were occasional activities to see too, such as burning off rank vegetation to encourage fresh verdure. Although there are references to this in old records they do not tell us whether this was a general practice. Burning the southern lowland heaths does not seem to have been used as widely as 'swaling' the moors. Records are often from legal proceedings when things have got out of control and do little to answer today's questions concerning the frequency or season. It leaves us presuming that in *most* places it

of the grasses and invading trees. Returning livestock to the heaths for grazing has entailed a degree of re-learning that which our ancestors had formerly passed on from generation to generation. In particular, conservationists wanted to know which types of animal would favour the particular plants needing control. To reduce rank vegetation at the beginning of a conservation programme cattle were found to devour everything down to the ground - where there is a choice of fodder Ling makes up about 20% of their diet. Ponies were excellent too as they take a greater bulk, being non-ruminant, and take much more woody material as they like to include coarse fibre in their diets. Sheep took off regenerating Birch saplings and goats went for the more woody Birch stems, by rearing up and catching them between their front legs to trap the sapling under their body as they returned to all fours for browsing everything off. The goats even browsed Scots Pine which other livestock tend to avoid. Cattle and ponies were best at the Purple Moor Grass and will take it to a total of some 75% of a mixed diet. As for Bracken, the heavier the animal the better because crushing the emerging croziers under the hoof is a very effective natural control, over a sustained period, and avoids using herbicides.

Wavy Hair Grass.

J.B.

was irregular, if at all. That knowledge would be important today to the conservationists wanting to know whether controlled burning would recreate past cycles by which to help conserve the heaths. On the whole it is felt that although the favoured vegetation does respond and burnt ground does suit some wildlife species, such as the Woodlark, the overall destruction of reptiles and invertebrates is unacceptable. A preferable means would be periodic cutting and scraping, where grazing is not feasible.

In complete contrast, another occasional scene, in some locations, was the passing through of drovers, from as far away as Wales. They brought cattle and sheep through the southern counties towards the London markets or to Maidstone. Many a trackway, rightly or wrongly, is still called the Drovers' Track or something similar. The one round the flank of the heaths above Frimley, Surrey, is still called *The Maultway* - from the Welsh *mollt*, for mutton, (now the B3015). In the early 19th century Frimley people still recalled being able to catch little black sheep which had been left behind accidentally by the drovers. Presumably the black ones were well camouflaged in the dark heath and more easily missed. The locals watched their own beasts to ensure they were not added to the droves.

Theft has always been a major threat and rustling still continues today. In pre-Reformation times that great land-owner, the Church, tried to deter rustlers by threat of excommunication - the ritual which, if carried out, would prevent the salvation of the souls of the damned sinners. In order that the implications of this should be fully understood and feared it was decreed in 1279, from Reading, by Archbishop Peckham, that parish priests should explain it to their people on the Sundays after every Rural Chapter and the Archdeacons were to see that this was done. Ironically, the very people who were expected to heed such dire warnings missed them. They were busy stealing livestock while everyone else was safely out of the way in church. From time to time parishes would therefore gather "with cross and candle and bell tolling" to hear that one of their neighbours was judged accursed by Holy Mother Church, after which the priest would throw down the candle, spit on the ground, and the bells rang out. All very dramatic but worth the risk to those who otherwise foresaw their death by starvation.

RIGHT: Early 19th century drover with his badge on his left arm. Imagine him in a white coat over a yellow waistcoat, with a red-spotted white neckerchief and stockings striped in blue and white.

SOURCES

Printed sources quoted once only are credited in the text. Those used more extensively or which add further information are listed below. Those with a * have lengthy bibliographies. Otherwise there would be a list of many pages for all the statements collected over the last thirty years but which would not in themselves contribute to further study. Much of the material was collected orally from surviving usages or memories of earlier times, just as was a great deal from old photograps and artwork in museum collections.

ACKNOWLEDGEMENTS

This study was only possible with the help of countless people over the last thirty years who have contributed to the data base from which the material was drawn. For specialist knowledge in checking and extending material for the book I am indebted to the following: for bees, Anne Buckingham, Surrey Beekeepers (Farnham) and Oliver Brown, Horsham and District Beekeepers; for birch wine, The Lurgashall Winery; for bracken, Dr Rona Pitman; for broom in horticulture, Cathal Ellis at the National Collection; for broom-makers, Norman Ratcliffe, Happy Families Ancestral Research; for soap, Pam Bowley; for current grazing projects, Paul Bruce of the Berkshire Heathland project and Dr. Robert McGibbon of the Surrey Heathland Project; for heathers in horticulture, David McClintock, President, and Daphne Everett, Secretary, of The Heather Society; Dr. Nick Michael, Heathland Project Manager, English Nature; Tim Price and Stephen Fry, Countryside Rangers.

The staff of the following libraries and institutions patiently answered enquiries and provided source materials: Borough of Surrey Heath Museum, Camberley; Borough of Elmbridge Museum, Weybridge; Forestry Research Station at Alice Holt, The National Trust, The Royal Horticultural Society, The Royal Pharmaceutical Society of Great Britain, and The Surrey Archaeological Society. Surrey County Library provided its usual fine service at getting photocopies of old sources and Laura Hastings at Dept. Economic Botany, Royal Botanic Gardens, Kew, traced and provided other rare books. For illustrations, Janet Blight, Pam Bowley, Beryl Daborn, Robert McGibbon. For much assistance with the text and proof reading, Theo Spring, Robert McGibbon and Gordon Weaver.

BIBLIOGRAPHY

Ashley House Building Accounts; Surrey Record Office.
AUBREY, John, *Natural History and Antiquities of the County of Surrey*; 1718-19, Repr. 1975, Kohler & Coombes, Dorking.
BOARD OF AGRICULTURE FOR SCOTLAND, 1917, *Bracken as a Source of Potash*, Leaflet No.39
BOSTON, C. *The History of Compton in Surrey*; Wightman, 1933.
BOTTOMLEY, Frank; *The Abbey Explorer's Guide*; Kaye & Ward; 1981
CAMPBELL, David, 'On Thatching with Fern', *Trans. Highland Soc. of Scotland*, 1831, Vol 2, pp184-90.

CHADWICK, L.*In Search of Heathlands*; Dennis Dobson; 1892*
CHILD, F.J.ed.; *The English and Scottish Popular Ballads*, 1882-89; 5 vols. Repr. Dover, New York, 1965.
COLLIER, John, 'Thatching with Heath', *Trans. Highland Soc. of Scotland*, 1831, Vol 2, pp190-5.
COOPER, M. AND JOHNSON, A.; *Poisonous Plants in Britain and their Effects Upon Animals and Man*, HMSO; 1984.*
COX, J.C., *Churchwardens' Accounts from the Fourteenth Century to the Close of the Seventeenth Century*; Methuen, 1913.
DIMBLEBY,G., *The Development of British Heathlands and their Soils*; Oxford; 1962.*
ELLIS, E. A.; *Wild Flowers of the Waterways and Marshes*; Jarrold; 1973.
EVELYN, John, *Silva: or, A Discourse of Forest-Trees etc.* 5th Ed. 1729
Acetaria; 1699
FREEMAN, George, *A History of Sunbury on Thames*; Sunbury & Shepperton Local Hist. Soc. 1981 ed.
GERARD, John; *The Herball or Generall Historie of Plantes*; Thomas Johnson ed. 1636.
GODWIN, Harry, *History of the British Flora*, Cambridge University Press, 2nd ed. 1975.*
HARVEY, John; 1972; *Early Gardening Catalogues*; Phillimore; 1972
HILL, Thomas; *The Gardener's Labyrinth*; 1577; Oxford University Press Ed. 1975.
HOFFMAN, D; *Welsh Herbal Medicine*; Abercastle Publications;1978
JEKYLL, Gertrude; *Old West Surrey*; Longmans; 1904.
KENYON, G.H., *The Glass Industry in the Weald*, Leicester University Press.1967
K'EOGH, John, *Botanalogia Universalis Hibernica*; Cork;1735.
LAFONT, A. *A Herbal Folklore*; Badger Books; Bideford; 1984.
LEWIS, William; *An Experimental History of the Materia Medica*, 4th ed. ed John Aitken, London 1791.
LUCAS, A..T, *Furze: A Survey and History of its Uses in Ireland*; Dublin, 1960.
MARTINDALE : *The Extra Pharmacopoeia*; Pharmaceutical Press; 30th Ed. 1993.*
MABEY, R.; *Flora Britannica*; Sinclair-Stevenson; 1996.
MILLSPAUGH, C.F.; *American Medicinal Plants*; 1892 repr. Dover Pub. ; New York; 1974.*
MORRIS, C., *The Journeys of Celia Fiennes*, Cresset Press.1947.
MOUNTFORD, F; *A Commoner's Cottage*; Allan Sutton Publishing Ltd. 1992.
PARKINSON, J., *Theatrum Botanicum*.1640.
RACKHAM, Oliver, *History of the Countryside*, Dent; 1986.*
RAFINESQUE, C.S., *Medical Flora or Manual of the United States;*Vol 2, Atkinson & Alexander; Philad.1830.
RYMER, L. 'The History and Ethnobotany of Bracken', *Journal of the Linnaean Society (Botany)*; 1976.
STACE, C. *New Flora of the British Isles*; Cambridge U.P. 1991.
STRATTON, H., *Ottershaw Through the Ages*; Pub. H. Stratton; 1990
YOUNG, Geoffrey; *Traditional British Crafts*; Marshall Cavendish; 1989

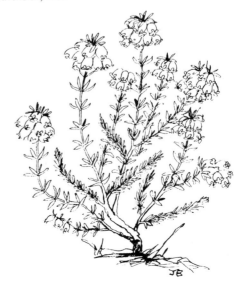

INDEX

Many small birds ended up in the cooking pot. Skylarks and Blackbirds were 2d a dozen in Tudor markets and kept that price for many generations.

Wheatear

95

For details of other publications and talks given to groups, please write to the publisher's address on p.2